Hawk-Moths

of Great Britain and Europe

Hawk-Moths

of Great Britain
and Europe

L. Hugh Newman

CASSELL · LONDON

CASSELL & COMPANY LTD
35 RED LION SQUARE, LONDON WC1
MELBOURNE · SYDNEY · TORONTO
JOHANNESBURG · CAPE TOWN · AUCKLAND

Printed in Great Britain
by Jarrold & Sons Ltd, Norwich

This book is dedicated to Hilary, Susan and Michael

Contents

Foreword

A book on our hawk-moths at last! A whole book to themselves as befits the noblest insects of them all. I forget now whether it was I who suggested the idea to Hugh Newman or whether I just meant to and made enthusiastic noises when he told me he was making the book. Either way there has long been a need for such a book and it is delightful to be allowed to be associated with this splendid tribute to one of my favourite groups of animals.

Hawk-moths have been a part of my life since I was nine years old. Their streamlined swept-winged perfection, the patrician dignity of their tail-spiked caterpillars, the delightful promise of those green shiny eggs, the wonder and mystery of that incredible metamorphosis—these had an infinite appeal in those far-off days, an appeal which happily remains undimmed.

On visiting a foreign land one of my first questions to a local naturalist is, 'What is your commonest hawk-moth?' In the distant Galapagos Islands I found the larvae of one of the nine native species in fantastic numbers. Every Lycium bush was covered with exquisitely patterned black and green caterpillars with deep crimson tail horns—and the caterpillars were of many different ages. It is the only time I have ever seen hawk-moths in 'pest proportions'.

Back in the days of my early youth I spent the summer on the French island of Noirmoutier off the mouth of the Loire, and there found the caterpillars of the Hummingbird Hawk-moth, feeding on succulent sea bedstraw, which grew over the sand-dunes. Forty years later I took my family back to Noirmoutier, and for some time I could not find the food plant again. After searching for half a mile along the dunes I came at last upon a patch of the bedstraw; I bent down with my son and daughter and there they were—one, two, eventually seven Hummingbird larvae. On the half-mile return walk we found many patches of food plant which I had overlooked on the way out, but no caterpillars on any of it.

Next day we found more food plant further along the dunes, but still no more caterpillars. On all that stretch of coast it seemed that they were only on the one patch where we had first looked, even though the moths themselves were buzzing about everywhere.

Alas in this country there are many fewer hawk-moths than there were in the days of my youth. Poplar, Eyed and Lime Hawks are all less numerous. I search now fruitlessly on rows of trees which formerly had the caterpillars on them in the right months year after year. Whether this decline can be attributed to the ubiquitous insecticides or to some other cause, we are all the poorer for the scarcity; for hawk-moths are a rewarding study. To rear them from the egg is simple and fascinating and there is still much to learn of their biology.

I hope this lovely book will lead many people, young and old, to the contemplation of their unique beauty, perhaps even to join the select band of hawk-moth addicts who have discovered their particular appeal.

PETER SCOTT

Slimbridge, October 1964

Illustrations

I duly acknowledge, with grateful thanks, the following photographers who have allowed me to reproduce their copyright photographs in this book, with special thanks to Stephen Dalton for all his close co-operation, and for the many pictures he took of my own bred specimens.

COLOUR PLATES

MONOCHROME

Acknowledgements

Many friends and colleagues in the field have contributed much valuable information from first-hand experience while I was compiling this book, and I should especially like to thank M. Claude Lemaire of Paris for allowing the hawk-moths in his collection to be especially photographed and for the notes he supplied on *Marumba quercus*, the Oak Hawk-moth he has on many occasions collected on the Côte d'Azur. The specimen of the hybrid moth *Smerinthus ocellata* × *Laothoe populi* was kindly loaned to me by Mr J. B. Purefoy and was bred by him in captivity. Without the help of Captain Hugh Ennion I would have had great difficulty in writing of the early stages of such species as *Acherontia atropos* and *Daphnis nerii*, as he had observed and bred both species while serving in Muscat with the Sultan's Armed Forces. Lastly Mr Austin Richardson's experiences while breeding *Herse convolvuli* were of great value to me. I also derived help in details of life histories not familiar to me from the works of J. W. Tutt and Dr A. Seitz, and notes by amateur breeders and collectors published over the last half century in *The Entomologist*, *The Entomologist's Gazette* and *The Entomologist's Record* provided much interesting information not readily available to the general public.

Without the help of my wife, all the work of research and proof reading might have become tedious, but with her unfailing enthusiasm the task was completed with enjoyment, which I hope shows in the writing.

I duly acknowledge, with grateful thanks, the photographers mentioned in the List of Illustrations who have allowed me to reproduce their copyright photographs in this book.

L. Hugh Newman

Betsoms,
Westerham,
Kent

Preface

This book is not intended to be a scientific treatise. I feel very strongly that the great majority of people who take an interest in the splendid hawk-moths do not wish to read lengthy accounts of their anatomical details or the intricacies of their classification. Such information can easily be found, if wanted, in the entomological libraries and the natural history museums. What I have tried to do is to give a readable account of these fine insects, and especially of their habits and behaviour as observed and recorded by myself and many other entomologists through the years.

Counting the hairs on a newly hatched caterpillar under a magnifying glass may be necessary in order to determine its exact place in the complicated relationship of insects, but to me such details are not important. What matters infinitely more is an understanding of the behaviour of moths in the various stages of their life cycle and in this field very many problems still wait to be solved. We do not even know why the Striped Hawk-moth or the rare Oleander Hawk feel compelled to leave the warmth of their native lands in the south to cross a continent and the English Channel in order to land in a country where they have no chance of survival. Perhaps one day we will find the answer to this and many other puzzling questions, but meanwhile the insects we study continue to live as their natural instincts dictate and we can only watch and wonder and perhaps, through careful observation, gradually gain a greater understanding.

To me the hawk-moths have always been the most fascinating of all the insects. Their size and beauty, their swift powerful flight and their ability to hover like birds of prey on quivering wings in the gathering darkness of a summer's evening have always given me tremendous pleasure. Observing the reaction of a Death's-head Hawk-moth placed on a honeycomb, or watching a Hummingbird Hawk feeding from the valerian in my garden on a sunny day, is an experience I infinitely prefer to the most stupendous film epic on a wide screen. And in this, I am sure, I am not alone. There must be a great many people who would rather find a grey Poplar Hawk on the doorstep than a sheaf of highly coloured brochures in their letter-box. It is for them that this book has been written, and I hope that both the text and the colour photographs of living moths and caterpillars will give both enjoyment and information.

Introduction

The hawk-moths, scientifically known as the *Sphingidae,* are a large family, diverse in shape and size and distributed all over the world. Sixty-odd species occur in the Palearctic region, but only nine of these can be called natives of Britain. Nine more reach this country as migrants or vagrants from time to time, some of them only very rarely, and there are some other southern and eastern European species which are not migratory in habit and therefore unlikely to be found in the wild north of the Channel.

In such a large family considerable individual variation occurs, and the hawk-moths can be divided up into several groups. The main division is between those which have well-developed tongues and are therefore able to feed from flowers, and those whose mouth parts are so undeveloped as to make feeding impossible. The latter are in the minority, but include the Poplar Hawk, the Lime Hawk, the Eyed Hawk and the southern European Oak Hawk-moth. The Bee Hawks, which are rather small in size, and with the exception of the eastern European *Hemaris croatica,* have transparent wings, form a group of their own, and both the Hummingbird Hawk-moth and the Death's-head have characteristics which set them apart from the others.

The one feature which all the hawk-moths have in common is the type of egg they lay. The size of the egg varies with different species and does not bear any direct relation to the size of the moth, the largest hawk-moths often laying remarkably small eggs; but they are practically always pale green in colour, nearly round, or somewhat oval in shape, slightly flattened from above and with smooth, transparent shells. The size of the eggs is not constant, even in individual moths, and the first eggs laid tend to be considerably larger than those which are laid towards the end of a female's life. Just before hatching the young caterpillar can be seen through the transparent shell.

On hatching the hawk-moth larvae usually eat at least part of their egg shells, although often only just enough to enable them to crawl out. When they first emerge from the shell they have on their bodies a number of tubercles, or raised warts, furnished with prominent hairs, often with forked tips, but these are hardly visible unless the caterpillars are observed under a magnifying glass. In the process of growth and development these tubercles disappear and instead their skins often develop what is usually described as a shagreen surface, covered with tiny raised spots with very short hairs, which again cannot be clearly distinguished by the naked eye.

The prominent horn on the twelfth segment is typical of most hawk-moth caterpillars, but in the case of the Small Elephant it is replaced by a small raised wart. The horn may be either rough, or smooth and shining, and differs in size and shape, but in the newly hatched larvae it is always of a disproportionate length, sometimes almost half as long as the body. As the larva grows, however, the horn becomes smaller in comparison with the body and in fully fed caterpillars it is seldom more than one tenth of the complete length, and often less than this.

Hawk-moth caterpillars differ a great deal in size and appearance. Generally speaking those which feed on trees and shrubs tend to be green and rather inconspicuous in their markings, whereas those which feed on low-growing herbaceous plants are more vividly coloured and often patterned with brightly contrasting spots and streaks. The southern species, which only arrive in Britain as migrants, have much more brightly coloured larvae than our native moths.

The increase in size, from the time of hatching until the larva is fully fed after three or four skin changes, is tremendous; careful experiments have shown that a Privet Hawk caterpillar, for example, weighs almost ten thousand times more when fully fed than when just hatched. This staggering increase in weight takes place very rapidly, during a period of no more than five or six weeks. Before pupating, however, there is a considerable loss in weight again and the pupa generally only weighs half as much as the fully fed caterpillar.

The number of moults varies, but normally the skin is cast four times before the caterpillar is ready to pupate. Often the old skin is eaten, at least partially, but this is not always the case. Some Sphingid larvae spin rather flimsy cocoons as a protection for their pupae, while others simply burrow into the ground and hollow out a chamber whose walls are strengthened by a fluid voided from the mouth. Several observers have also noticed fully fed caterpillars anointing their bodies with this fluid very soon after they finish feeding, but the exact purpose of this is not known. It may possibly help to darken the skin so that the caterpillar is less conspicuous when it begins to wander along the ground in search of a pupation site.

If a hawk-moth is carefully watched while the change from the caterpillar to pupa is taking place, it will be seen that the characteristic stripes and markings of the larva are still visible on the pupal shell immediately after the caterpillar skin has been shed, but they quickly disappear as the pupa darkens from green or yellow to the final dark or light brown colour. In those hawk-moths which have a well-developed tongue, this can be clearly seen on the pupal shell, either encased in a keel like a projection or actually enclosed in a separate sheath, such as the well-known 'jug handle' of the Convolvulus Hawk pupa. This 'proboscis' on the pupa gradually extends after the larval skin has been cast and while the pupal shell is still soft, the process taking an hour or so to complete. The pupae of most hawk-moths are very mobile and will twist and jerk strongly when handled. They are also furnished with a series of flanges on the surface of the abdominal segments, which help them to wriggle into a favourable position for emerging, or assist in keeping the pupal shell immobile while the moth forces its way out.

When a hawk-moth is about to emerge the pupal shell splits across the back of the head and down along the front edge of the wings, enabling the moth to free itself. The process of drying the wings takes about an hour, and during this time the wings are held back, very much like the wings of butterflies at rest, except that they do not actually touch each other. When drying is completed, the wings are folded in the characteristic attitude, which varies with the species. In Poplar Hawks and Eyed Hawks the frenulum, which is the loop and bristle arrangement that links the fore-wing and hind-wing together in flight, is not properly developed and while at rest the moths hold their wings in such a way that the front edge of the hind-wing is visible in front of the fore-wing, an attitude which would be impossible if the wings were linked together. The Lime Hawk does not take up this exaggerated position and has an effective linking arrangement, and in the other hawk-moths, which, unlike the Poplar and Eyed Hawks, are very skilful and rapid in flight, the frenulum is well developed in both sexes. When at rest these moths settle with the wings folded over their bodies rather in the shape of a roof, like the Privet Hawk and the Death's-head, or pointing backwards at an angle of about seventy degrees, which gives them the shape of a broad arrow head.

In all the fast-flying hawk-moths which hover in front of flowers while feeding, the wings are long and narrow with plain, undented margins. The fore-wings are pointed at the tip and the hind-wings are rather small. In the Poplar Hawk, the Eyed Hawk and the Oak Hawk-moth the wings are broader and have wavy edges and the hind-wings are comparatively large. The same rule applies to a lesser degree to the Lime Hawk, and the Death's-head, which feeds, but does not hover, has more rounded fore-wings and larger hind-wings and generally a much less streamlined appearance than say the Convolvulus Hawk or the Striped Hawk. The flower feeders also tend to have narrower and more pointed bodies, but this does not apply to the Bee Hawks or the Hummingbird Hawk, whose bodies are rather broad and made even wider by tufts of hair.

The length of time occupied by the complete life cycle of a hawk-moth, from the egg to the perfect insect, varies with the species and often with the season of the year. The eggs hatch in anything from seven to eight days to three weeks, depending to some extent on the prevailing temperature, and the larvae normally complete their growth in six or eight weeks or even in just over a month. Often the caterpillars do not change into pupae immediately after 'going down' or making their cocoons on the surface of the ground, and instances have been recorded of larvae remaining inert for three weeks or more before finally casting their skins. The period in the pupal stage varies a great deal. The hawk-moths which are indigenous to Africa normally spend only a short time as pupae and may emerge within a month of pupating, and this is also the case with the double-brooded species even in more northern latitudes, although the second generation remains in the pupal stage for seven or eight months. Other, single-brooded species spend nine months of the year as pupae and occasionally this period may be extended to twelve months or even to two years.

The only European hawk-moth which hibernates as an adult is the Hummingbird Hawk. None of them hibernate as eggs or larvae. The life span of an adult moth depends very much on the weather conditions and the food situation. The non-feeding hawks seldom survive more than ten days to a fortnight, but those which feed on nectar can live for several weeks if the weather is good and plenty of suitable flowers are available. Convolvulus Hawk-moths have been kept alive in captivity for as long as six weeks and the tremendous migratory journeys they accomplish are proof of a long life and great stamina.

Hawk-moths have many enemies and comparatively few of the eggs laid ever reach maturity. Both eggs and larvae are frequently parasitized, both by Hymenopterous and Dipterous wasps and flies, the larvae are eaten by birds and predatory insects, especially by the common wasp, and pupae fall prey to small mammals as well as to birds and carnivorous beetles. The adult moths are usually fairly well protected by their camouflage during the day, but are eagerly snapped up by bats at night.

With the exception of the Bee Hawks and the Hummingbird Hawk, most of the Sphingids do not normally fly before sunset unless they are migrating. The evening flight generally begins just at dusk and continues for a comparatively short time, and another flight period occurs again at dawn. Mating usually takes place during the evening flight. Some moths stay paired for twenty-four hours, while others part during the night, and the females very soon begin to lay their eggs.

In those moths which do not feed, the eggs are fully developed when the female emerges from the pupal shell and they are laid very rapidly in a matter of four or five days after mating. In those species which feed on nectar, the development of the eggs is gradual, depending on the amount of food the female moth can find, and they are laid over an extended period which may cover several weeks. Parthenogenesis, or the ability of unmated females to lay fertile eggs, is not common among the hawk-moths, but there have been several well-authenticated instances when this has happened with Poplar Hawks, Lime Hawks and Eyed Hawks as well as with Privet Hawks. Occasionally hybrids are found in nature, and a great many have been produced under artificial conditions.

Although the hawk-moths cannot compare with the silk-moths in size, they are nevertheless among the largest of the moths and their powers of flight are second to none. Before they take to the wing after a long period of rest, they vibrate their wings very rapidly, in order to raise the body temperature sufficiently to make sustained flight possible. While flying most of them produce a distinct buzzing or humming sound, caused by the extremely rapid movement of the wings. All the night-flying species are attracted to light and can be caught without difficulty in mercury light traps, or even by using an ordinary powerful electric light.

The Privet Hawk

SPHINX LIGUSTRI

Haunts. The Privet Hawk, which is generally quoted as the example of a typical hawk-moth, occurs throughout Europe, reaching north to Scotland, Scandinavia and Finland. It is not found in Spain and is rarer in eastern Europe than in regions further west. In Great Britain it is a common moth, especially so in the south. It may be seen both in the country, especially on chalky downland where wild privet grows naturally, in villages, small country towns and in the suburbs of large cities. It is abundant in many sea-side towns. The adult moths often visit flowers at dusk in search of nectar.

The Egg. The Privet Hawk lays a light green egg, elliptical in shape and measuring about 2 mm in length and $1\frac{1}{2}$ mm across. It is smooth, but not especially glossy. The eggs are fixed on the leaves, or sometimes on the stems of the food plant, both on the upper and lower surface, usually singly, but now and then in little groups of twos or threes. The time of hatching varies from ten days to a fortnight or more, if the weather is cool.

The Caterpillar. On hatching the caterpillar measures just over $\frac{1}{2}$ cm in length and the tail horn is almost as long as the body. The colouring is at first a pale yellow with a hint of green, but as soon as the larva begins to feed the skin becomes darker and very soon takes on the clear, almost luminous green which is characteristic of this species. A well-grown, fully fed caterpillar is 10 cm long and about $4\frac{1}{2}$ cm in girth. The body is cylindrical in shape, tapering very slightly towards the head and the prominent tail horn, which has a slight downward curve, is nearly 1 cm long, and is glossy and black on top and pale yellow underneath. The ground colour is a beautiful apple green, slightly darker on the first four segments and on the under surface. The body is decorated, along either side, with seven white sloping stripes, edged with violet, which deepens to a rich purple at the lower end. The spiracles are light

1

orange and the head has a fairly wide black stripe on each side of the face. The legs and sucker feet are almost black. In 1947 a full-grown larva with a second, shorter horn below the normal one, was found at Folkestone.

The Pupa. The rich brown pupa of the Privet Hawk is about 5 cm long and 4 cm in girth and arched along the back. The prominent tongue case measures just over $\frac{1}{2}$ cm in length and is separated from the rest of the body. The skin of the pupa is slightly rough, but still somewhat glossy, and the body ends in a sharp point. A living pupa will move if it is handled.

The Adult Moth. The Privet Hawk is the largest of the native British hawk-moths, and may measure over 11 cm in wing-span, with a body length of 4 to 5 cm. The wings are pointed and the front edge of the fore-wings is curved towards the tip, while the outer margin is straight. The predominant colour of the fore-wings is brown, with streaks of grey and a few black lines. The hind-wings are a pale, milky pink with bands of black running parallel to the edge. The body is banded in bright pink and black with a central stripe of grey, and with an interrupted black streak in the middle. The thorax bears a large patch of very dark brown, with grey hairs in the centre. The antennae, which are held tightly against the sides of the body at rest, are white and slender and each one ends in a stiff hair. On the underside the wings are a pale greyish-brown, crossed by broad black bars, which on the hind-wings are out-lined in a pale greyish-white, with the faintest hint of pink. The body is also grey-brown.

The English name of this large and beautiful hawk-moth is self-explanatory and derives from its most common food plant the privet (*Ligustrum*) as does its specific Latin name. The generic name of *Sphinx* refers to the caterpillar, which assumes, while resting during the day, an extraordinary and very characteristic attitude. Clinging to its food plant with pro-legs and hind-claspers only, the larva bends the rest of its body almost at right angles to the support and hunches the first few segments so that the head itself is curved forward and the whole creature, seen in profile, rather resembles the outline of an Egyptian sphinx. In nature the caterpillar almost invariably hangs like this upside down, clinging to the underside of a leaf, or occasionally to an upright twig, but it never settles with the head uppermost. Unfortunately mistakes are often made in reproducing photographs the wrong way round so that the larva appears to be sitting up and begging like a dog, which in fact it never does.

In its natural upside-down position the white stripes are edged with purple 'shadows' underneath, thus giving the impression of a glinting leaf surface which is shaded below. The larva blends into the surroundings, and in spite of its great size is not easily noticed. Although Privet Hawk larvae do not normally show any great variation in colour, apart from slight differences in the shade of green, there are two details which can vary considerably in examples found in the wild. The anal horn may have very little, or even no pale straw colour; and the diagonal stripes vary from a pale mauve, through to a deep purple edged with black. An unusual variety of the stripes is one in which there is a second stripe of purple and black, below and behind the lower end of each normal stripe. A number of larvae, over forty, bearing these heavily marked double stripes, were found feeding close together on uncut privet hedges of a small council estate in Tollesbury, Essex, in August 1962, by my friend George Temple. So many similarly marked larvae in a small area indicates that the markings were probably an hereditary trait carried by one female moth. As well as feeding on privet and lilac (*Syringa vulgaris*), the larvae have also been found on ash (*Fraxinus*), holly (*Ilex*), guelder rose (*Viburnum*), spindle (*Euonymus*) and dogwood (*Cornus*) and on several occasions in gardens on honeysuckle (*Lonicera*). The larvae feed mainly at night and many breeders have noticed that those which have been reared on lilac produce bigger and heavier pupae than those reared on other food plants.

The side stripes appear after the first moult and are at the beginning simply lines of pale dots. In the third instar they become yellow with just a touch of purple near the centre and in the fourth instar the violet colour extends all along the stripe. The larva takes six or seven weeks to feed up, and when it leaves the food plant and begins to wander in search of a suitable site for pupation, the clear green colour changes to a dull greenish-brown, like a bruised apple, and the purple stripes become paler and less noticeable. In this guise the caterpillar can crawl along the ground without looking too conspicuous, and as it often wanders a considerable distance before burrowing, the colour change is of great importance. It is, however, no protection against ants and in localities where the big wood ant (*Formica rufa*) is numerous, as for example in Finland, I have seen wandering Privet Hawk larvae attacked and killed by swarms of ants which then cut them to pieces and carry the remains to their nests.

The Privet Hawk burrows deeper than our other native hawk-moths and may sometimes go down five or six inches if the soil is soft and friable. It does not spin a cocoon, but merely hollows out a small

3

chamber. Normally the larvae pupate towards the end of August or in September, but late stragglers are sometimes found and in 1951 a half-grown larva was picked up on a farm in Essex as late as 7th November. The period in the pupa is usually about nine and a half months but instances are known of pupae lying dormant for two or even three years before emerging.

The normal flight period is in June, but occasionally a few moths are on the wing already in May and others do not appear until July. Privet Hawks nearly always crawl out of their shells during the night, or early in the morning, after wriggling up close to the surface of the soil. The moths at once search for some upright support where they can cling while their wings expand. As soon as they have dried, the wings are folded over the body, like the roof of a house, so that only the dark forewings are visible and in this position the moth remains immobile until dusk.

The Privet Hawk is a swift and powerful flier and the noise of its vibrating wings, when recorded and amplified, sounds like the engine of a motor-cycle before the clutch is slipped in and it moves off. Unlike the Poplar, the Eyed Hawk and the Lime Hawk, which do not visit flowers, the Privet Hawk, with its long tongue, is greedy for nectar, and may often be seen hovering in front of flowering privet, honeysuckle or valerian.

During and immediately after the war, when so many gardens in suburban London were totally neglected, Privet Hawks were extremely common and the caterpillars abounded on the untrimmed and overgrown privet hedges round bombed buildings. Since then they have decreased in numbers, but the Privet Hawk caterpillar is still the hawkmoth which is most often found and brought to myself and other entomologists for identification. The fact that the larvae usually feed only a few feet above ground level makes it fairly easy to find, and the moth also appears with great regularity in mercury vapour moth traps during the season when it is on the wing.

The Privet Hawk-moth does not hang suspended from a twig like the smaller hawk-moths, but prefers to rest on something more solid, a tree trunk or a fairly thick stem or branch, a wall, a gate-post, a garden seat or something similar. It is in places like this that the mated pairs are found, tail to tail, both with their feet resting on the surface of their support. Although they do not take to the wing again until after dusk, they often part during the afternoon and move an inch or so away from each other. The female begins to lay the following night and being a large moth she may deposit as many as two hundred and fifty eggs,

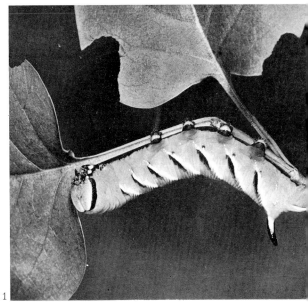

Lilac is an alternative food for the Privet Hawk caterpillar and very fine specimens can be reared in captivity on this diet. The remarkable photograph below shows a moth disturbed during the day and taking off from a privet bush.

×1

×1½

over a period of a week or more, and during this time she often visits flowers for nectar.

The sexes are identical in colouring and shape but the female is generally a little longer and slightly thicker in the body and her antennae are more slender than those of the male. The moths are, on the whole, very uniform in appearance, although they differ considerably in size, but occasional aberrations do occur. The form known as *pallida*, in which the pink colouring is replaced by cream, has been found several times and in 1939 a collector bred two moths of this type from wild larvae collected on holly in the New Forest. They were both males. The late Neville Chamberlain also had one of these moths, with a Birmingham data label, in his collection. Sometimes moths are found with fore-wings much paler than normal and now and then the hind-wings lack the dark bands.

Because of its large size and the comparative ease with which it can be bred and fed in captivity, the Privet Hawk is used extensively for research. In recent years both University College London and Karolinska Institutet in Stockholm have conducted research programmes with the aid of Privet Hawks. The Swedish project, which is an investigation into the mechanism of the eye and its reaction to light and darkness, has been assisted by a grant from the U.S.A. Air Force because of possible applications to problems of night flying.

The Pine Hawk

HYLOICUS PINASTRI

Haunts. This moth has a wide distribution throughout Europe in areas where the Scots pine, *Pinus sylvestris*, grows. It is common in Germany, Poland and northern Russia, and occurs all over Scandinavia and Finland, in parts of France and in Switzerland up to 1,650 feet altitude. It also breeds in certain parts of Great Britain, especially in Suffolk and in Hampshire, and appears to be spreading through Sussex and Surrey into Kent, but whether it is a true native or was introduced originally from the Continent is not known. The moth is found in and around the edges of pine woods, generally resting on the trunks of the trees.

The Egg. The egg is unusual for a hawk-moth, because instead of being green it is yellow with a tinge of reddish-brown. It has been compared in colouring to a white-heart cherry. It is slightly flattened and oval, measuring about 2 mm in length. The eggs are laid singly but often fairly near each other, on the needles or young twigs. Before hatching the dark head of the embryo larva can be seen through the transparent shell. The period of incubation varies from about a fortnight to eighteen or twenty days.

The Caterpillar. The Pine Hawk caterpillar is a typical hawk-moth larva with a well-developed horn. The head is rather large and clearly offset from the body, which is slender and of equal thickness throughout its length. In the fully grown caterpillar the segments are distinctly divided from each other and each segment in its turn is sub-divided into eight very narrow sections, separated by dark, sunken lines, so that the caterpillar appears to consist of a great number of very narrow rings joined together. In the final skin the larvae may be either green with a distinct wavy brown line along the centre of the back, two whitish stripes along each side and a yellow stripe just below the spiracles, or predominantly brown, very closely resembling the bark of the twigs. The legs are rather pale, the horn black and rough and the head reddish

7

with a yellow stripe edged with black. On the second segment, just behind the head is a slightly raised shield, striped in yellow and black. The skin is perfectly smooth and the head, under surface, legs and shield are glossy, as if varnished, and this almost oily appearance extends to the entire body when the larva darkens in colour just before pupating. Fully fed it measures 8 cm in length.

The Pupa. The pupa is slender and dark mahogany brown, with the tongue encased in a prominent sheath, which however is not separated from the body surface. The pupal shell is smooth, but not glossy, and the pupa measures just over 4 cm in length. The larva burrows into the ground before pupating and the pupa is active and mobile when touched. On the Continent the Pine Hawk is double brooded and a proportion of those bred in England in captivity also emerge the same season and breed again, and possibly this also happens in the wild. The pupae fairly often lie over from one year to the next, spending two winters in the dormant stage.

The Adult Moth. The Pine Hawk is the last of our indigenous moths to emerge and does not appear on the wing until June or even July. In colouring it is a soft dark grey all over, sprinkled on the fore-wings with paler grey scales and clouded with indistinct bands of a darker grey. There are also short well-defined streaks of very dark grey, three of them between the nervures near the centre of each wing, and one curved line near the tip. The hind-wings are brownish-grey, becoming lighter towards the base where they join the body. A very narrow band of alternate white and grey-brown 'beading' runs along the outer margin of both pairs of wings. The thorax is grey and there is a dark streak on each side of the abdomen which has a grey central line and is marked alternately with black and white. The hind legs are spotted with white and the antennae are white above and brownish below. The moth is fairly large, measuring some 9 cm in wing-span, and when at rest folds its wings over the body in the same way as the Privet Hawk-moth.

A certain amount of mystery surrounds the Pine Hawk in Britain and it is only during the last thirty years or so that it has become really well established and begun to spread. It was first mentioned among British insects in Donovan's work *A Natural History of British Insects* published in 1800, but the author simply wrote very briefly that it was reported to have been found on occasion in Scotland. In 1860 and again in 1861 a larva was found in the Isle of Mull, but since then there have been no more records from that part of the world. In the same year, 1860, a moth was found at Romsey in Hampshire, and then odd specimens were seen from time to time in various parts of the country, generally in the south.

From the 1880s onwards, more and more reports began to come in from East Anglia and although many of the most eminent entomologists of the day suspected that the moths had been 'planted' in the region and were of Continental origin, this was never proved, and by 1895 the Pine Hawk was apparently so common in parts of Suffolk, especially round Aldeburgh and Woodbridge, that larvae could be beaten from the trees. Entomologists had to admit the possibility that the Pine Hawk had been there for centuries, although undiscovered, or had possibly migrated from the Continent or arrived as a stowaway on some trading ship. Today we know no more than did J. W. Tutt when he wrote in 1886: 'We are no nearer to any exact knowledge of the date when *S. pinastri* first came to Britain, whether before that time that the North Sea separated us from the Continent (a few thousand years ago), whether with the first artificial introduction of its food plant into Suffolk (probably several hundred years ago), or with a later importation of firs, or by means of a more recent immigration. All these are things which resolve themselves into guess work, but have no scientific value whatever.' The fact that larvae of Suffolk stock tend to be more sombre in colouring in the final skin than the progeny of pupae imported from Germany, seems to indicate that they are a somewhat local form which may have been isolated for a long time.

In the 1930s the moth appeared at Saxmundham and Southwold and has since been discovered in Norfolk, and at about the same time it began to be more and more plentiful in Dorset and Hampshire, especially round Bournemouth. From this area it has spread, fairly rapidly, both to the north and east and is now found in many parts of Sussex and Surrey and even on the borders of Kent, as well as in the northern parts of Hampshire and even in Wiltshire. It has also been found in the Isle of Wight. At a time when so many insects are becoming more and more scarce, it is very encouraging to know that at least one of the British hawk-moths is rapidly increasing its range. As the moths emerge over a long period the larvae may be found feeding throughout the latter part of July, August and September, and second brood specimens even in October.

The Pine Hawk begins to fly at dusk and eagerly visits flowers, especially honeysuckle, hovering in front of the blooms and inserting its long tongue to probe for nectar. I have a very vivid memory of watching them in Finland, visiting the honeysuckle trained up the walls of the wooden house where I was staying. It was surrounded by pine forests and every evening at least half a dozen moths could be seen at the flowers in the twilight.

The females do not usually fly until they have mated and as they generally climb up the trunks of the pine trees to dry their wings, it is here that the mated pairs are most usually found. One entomologist, hunting for Pine Hawks in the Saxmundham area many years ago, happened to speak to a gipsy boy and found to his surprise that the lad knew the moths and told him that he had often found them high up in the trees. I have also discovered them on small seedling pines, only a foot or so above ground level, with their wings almost wrapped round the stems so that they look like a grey swelling on the bark. On the lower portion of a pine trunk, where the rough, splitting bark has turned a dark grey, the moths are extremely well camouflaged.

Although the pairs normally stay close together for twenty-four hours, they often separate during the afternoon, moving an inch or so apart, and as soon as it grows dark the male flies off to feed, while the female begins to lay her eggs. She too stops to feed at intervals and the egg laying is not completed for some days. Normally each female lays about a hundred eggs. They are at first a very pale, almost butter yellow, and the brown shading does not develop for a couple of days. The larvae always eat part of the egg shells on hatching and at first they are a dull yellow and measure about 4 mm in length. The head looks disproportionately large and heavy and is marked with brown. The horn, which has two points, quickly becomes dark at the tip. The larva begins by nibbling at the surface of a needle but as it grows it becomes able to eat it completely, starting from the tip and holding the needle between its legs while it bites off pieces until it reaches the base, and then beginning again on another one. Older needles are always preferred to the tender shoots.

Soon after it begins to feed the caterpillar turns green and when the first moult is completed the ground colour of the body becomes dark green, with six longitudinal creamy-yellow lines. The large head is a paler green than the body, with a dark streak on each side. At this stage, when sitting lengthways on the pine needles, the larvae are extremely

*Four successive stages in the
development of a Pine Hawk-moth after
it has crawled out of its pupal shell.*

×2

difficult to find as they blend remarkably well with their surroundings, especially when the sun is shining. After the second and third moult the caterpillars remain roughly the same in appearance, except that the pale lines become rather broader and the horn takes on a reddish tint. The legs and hind-claspers also turn pink and the spiracles are marked with red.

After the fourth moult the very distinct transverse divisions already mentioned become evident, both in the green and the brown form of the larva, and before pupating the caterpillars take on a purplish-grey tint. While they are feeding they are, on the whole, rather sluggish, and although they feed in daylight, they do not move about more than necessary in order to reach fresh supplies of food when those nearby are exhausted. When fully fed, however, they become restless, and after making their way down from the trees they often wander some distance in search of a pupating place, but whenever possible they burrow down among the pine needles at the base of the tree. I once picked up a fully fed larva on a pavement in Southbourne where it was unable to 'go down'.

Among the pines, the caterpillars feed for preference on *Pinus sylvestris*, but they have also been found occasionally on *Pinus pinaster* and on the two cedars *Cedrus libani* and *Cedrus deodara*. On the Continent a large proportion of the larvae are parasitized by the large *Ichneumon pisorius*, which emerges through a hole made in the side of the pupal shell, some time before the moth would normally be fully developed.

The two sexes are identical, but in the male the antennae are very slightly thicker. Individuals vary somewhat in size and markings and the darker grey shading and streaks may be more or less prominent, or sometimes almost absent so that the wings are nearly a uniform grey. Really striking aberrations are very rare, but a Scottish entomologist named McTaggart bred a whole series of albino forms which were the colour of pale milky coffee.

The Lime Hawk

MIMAS TILIAE

Haunts. The Lime Hawk is quite common over most of Europe, especially in Germany, and is also found in Denmark and southern Sweden. In the Alps its range extends to 1,500 feet. In Great Britain it occurs mainly in the south but has also been found in Yorkshire and very occasionally in Scotland. The very few specimens of this moth taken in Ireland have all been found in Galway, and may possibly have been imported. It is particularly abundant in the home counties, south and south-east of London, probably because in these suburban areas many streets and roads are still planted with avenues of lime trees. Country towns and parklands are other favourite haunts.

The Egg. The egg is decidedly oval, distinctly flattened and about 1·9 mm long. The shell is glossy and of a pale olive-green tint. A female may lay anything up to two hundred eggs either on lime trees or on elms, but they are extremely difficult to find in the wild. In a breeding cage the eggs are laid impartially on the sides of the cage or on the food provided and the normal period between laying and hatching is about three weeks, although in very warm weather it may be considerably shorter. There are, in fact, records of eggs hatching in ten days.

The Caterpillar. Newly hatched Lime Hawk larvae are pale green, about 6 mm long and their tail horns are equal to a third of the body length. They are very active at this stage and generally wander about a good deal before they begin to feed. In the early stages they are remarkably slender and even in the last instar they are slimmer than most other hawk-moth larvae. In the last skin, which is slightly rough and light green, the body tapers noticeably towards the head, and is decorated with seven diagonal yellow stripes, each with a patch of red just in front of the centre. In the full-grown larva the tail horn is comparatively short, clear blue above and red and yellow beneath, and there is a characteristic red and yellow patch on the anal flap just below the horn. A well-nourished Lime Hawk larva may reach a length of just over 6 cm in the last instar.

The Pupa. The caterpillar does not burrow very deep and the pupae are usually found quite close to the surface, among tussocks of grass or other rubbish at the foot of large trees. The pupa is a very dark brown, with a slightly reddish tinge. It generally measures just over 3 cm in length and the same in girth. The surface is rough to the touch with a sharp spine at the tail end.

The Adult Moth. The Lime Hawk is extremely variable both in colour and pattern. The irregular spots on the fore-wing are normally a dark olive, on a ground colour of buff, often with a slightly reddish tinge, and there is usually a whitish patch near the tip of the wing. The colour of the body generally more or less matches the ground colour of the wings, but the abdomen is of a darker shade. The hind-wings are a light brown, shading into olive towards the outer margin and with a distinct olive-green patch at the lower edge. The antennae are white above and brown beneath, with hooked bristles at the tips. On the underside the wings are a pale olive-green with a flush of pale rusty brown on the fore-wings. Both pairs of wings have a pale band running across them from the front edge to the hind margin. The legs are purplish-brown and the body a pale grey-green.

The Lime Hawk-moth derives its name from the food plant of the caterpillars, which feed principally on lime trees and appear to thrive equally well on the various species cultivated in parks and gardens. Another common food plant is elm and occasionally caterpillars have been found on birch, but on neither of these food plants do they feed up as rapidly as on lime. The extensive planting of lime trees in the suburbs of London at the beginning of this century favoured the Lime Hawk and although it is now less plentiful than it used to be, it is still a common moth. The custom of pollarding the trees in no way interferes with its breeding and the new shoots begin to sprout just at the time when the moth appears on the wing in May. The time of emergence naturally varies a little from year to year, depending on the weather, but the first Lime Hawks are usually on the wing soon after the middle of May and late specimens can still be found occasionally at the end of June.

The slender larvae grow rather slowly at first, and at the time of the first moult, about a week after hatching, they are just over 1 cm in length. They invariably rest during the daytime on the under surface of a leaf and feed at night. While they are young they do not sit straight along a rib of the leaf as they do later, but nearly always keep their bodies curved to one side, like a question mark. The tail horn at first has two points, but after the second moult it becomes a normal single horn with a rather dark tip. The head, which is clearly offset from the body, has a two-pointed crown tinged with red.

As the caterpillar grows the diagonal stripes on the body become more prominent and change from cream to yellow. After the third moult the short red oblique marks beside the stripes, begin to appear, but do not develop their full size and brightness until the last instar, when they show up very vividly against the yellow-green of the skin. The fully fed larva is very attractive and colourful, especially after the tail becomes blue.

As a young boy I often used to accompany my father in the evenings when he liked to walk around the streets in our neighbourhood looking for Lime Hawk larvae. His method was to attach a cut-throat razor to a light pole, about seven or eight feet long, and use this for severing the twigs which were out of reach in the normal way. I was given an acetylene lamp to carry and by directing the beam up among the branches of the pollarded lime along the road, it was possible to spot the larvae on the undersides of the leaves. I became quite adept at catching the falling twigs with one hand. Nowadays a long-handled pruner is a more convenient and less dangerous tool and a powerful long-beam torch easier to deal with than an acetylene lamp.

The Lime Hawk larva undergoes a very distinct change in appearance before pupating. The clear light green disappears and is replaced by a dull pink flesh colour, especially on the underside of the body, the red marks fade away and the upper surface becomes a livid grey-brown, often with a touch of blue. Instead of being slightly rough, the larva now feels quite smooth to the touch and it gradually shrinks in size. This process takes some days and while it is going on the caterpillar stops feeding and descends from the tree to look for a pupating site.

Normally the pupae are found at ground level, either among rubbish on the surface, or buried not more than an inch or so below it, but there are quite a number of records of pupae being discovered in chinks of the bark, especially on elms whose rough trunks afford suitable crevices. They have also been found in stacked flower pots and among sacks left underneath a lime tree in a garden. The final change does not take place immediately and six or even seven days may pass before the last larval skin is cast to reveal the pupa. Collectors sometimes take the trouble to fork over the soil at the base of lime trees, so as to prepare a suitable pupation site and tempt the descending caterpillars to burrow as soon as they reach the ground.

In localities where the moths are known to breed in some numbers, and especially if larvae have been noticed feeding rather high up in the trees, this is often worth while. But even without any preparation of this kind the pupae can sometimes be found quite easily. One entomologist collected no less than sixty pupae one winter in south-east London after the last war. Compared to most of the other hawk-moths the Lime Hawk pupa is rather small and there is seldom any sign of movement after the shell has hardened. The surface is dull and rough and the wingcases, which are clearly visible, appear unusually short. There is only a very slight tapering towards the head.

The moths do not seem to emerge at any special hour and in captivity they can be seen breaking out of their shells at any time. Some years ago a well-known entomologist recorded seeing a newly emerged Lime Hawk in a London street just before five o'clock in the afternoon. While the wings are expanding they are folded over the back so that the under surface can be seen if the moth is viewed from the side, but as soon as they are completely dry they are moved into the typical position on either side of the body, with the fore-wings almost completely covering the hind-wings. The curved front edge and the scalloped outer margin, combined with the disruptive pattern, give a good camouflage among leaves, but a newly emerged moth sitting on a tree trunk or a fence is fairly easily noticed.

The Lime Hawk is a very variable insect and therefore of special interest to collectors. The ground colour of the wings may range from a very light buff or yellow through many shades of green to a dull pale red or a rich brick red or even dark brown, and the markings may be almost any colour from brown to dark green or even a velvety red. The hind-wings also vary in the same way and there are about thirty named aberrations as well as many more which have not been given any special scientific name. Asymmetrical moths are not unusual and in 1952 my father, L. W. Newman, bred a halved gynandromorph.

In general there is little difference between the sexes among hawk-moths, but in the Lime Hawk the male and female can be easily distinguished. In normal specimens, the ground colour of the wings is tinged with pale brick red in the female, while the male is decidedly green. In the male the abdomen is also strongly curved upwards while in the female it is held more or less straight and the body is much thicker while full of eggs. The colours of the Lime Hawk tend to fade with time and old cabinet specimens therefore do not give a good idea of the appearance of this attractive insect when freshly emerged.

The Lime Hawk does not fly during the day even if disturbed, but hangs, head upwards, motionless until dusk. Soon after the light begins to fade, but while it is still possible to see things fairly clearly, the moths begin to move and after an initial whirring of wings, they take to the air. The virgin females remain still, releasing their assembling scent, while waiting for the males to arrive. In districts where the moths are common, numerous wild males will often assemble to a caged female during the first half hour after dusk. The mated pairs remain joined, quite still, for about twenty hours, the female facing upwards, the male often hanging free, head down, the tips of their wings touching. The following afternoon, the male drops down to the ground and then flies away and after a short time the female also takes to the wing and begins to search for the correct food plant on which to lay her eggs. The Lime Hawk does not visit flowers, but like the majority of moths it is involuntarily drawn towards a strong light, and many specimens are taken annually in mercury vapour moth traps.

The Eyed Hawk

SMERINTHUS OCELLATA

Haunts. The Eyed Hawk is widely distributed over most of central and northern Europe and extends its range right down to the Mediterranean. In Switzerland it reaches 1,600 feet, and it occurs commonly in the British Isles, except in Scotland where it is rare. It is however rather a local moth in its habits, and although it may be found year after year in the same place, it may be absent from other neighbouring localities which appear equally suitable. Gardens and wasteland, orchards and river banks, coastal sandhills, country lanes and coppices where either poplar, sallow, willow or apple trees grow, are the sort of places where the moth is likely to be found.

The Egg. The eggs, which are always laid singly and usually on the under surface of a leaf are pale yellowish-green and slightly oval, about $1\frac{1}{2}$ mm in length and are usually fixed midway between the edge of the leaf and the mid-rib. The females normally lay only a few eggs on each bush or tree, so that in nature the larvae are never crowded. A large healthy female can lay as many as 250 eggs over a period of four or five days. There is even a record of one female laying 351 eggs in captivity and dying with 38 eggs still remaining in her body. They hatch eleven to twenty days after laying, depending on the temperature.

The Caterpillar. On hatching the larva measures $\frac{1}{2}$ cm in length and has a slender, pale pink horn with a forked tip. The colour is at first a rather pale yellowish-green, but soon becomes more whitish-green. When fully fed the caterpillar measures some 8 cm in length and the rough skin is covered in tiny white raised dots. Immediately behind the head, on segments two to four, there is a horizontal white line along the side, followed by seven diagonal white lines, the last one running into the tail. Each of these lines is offset by an edging of green, which is rather darker in tone than the ground colour of the body. The tail horn, which is very slightly curved, has a small black tip but is other-

18

wise blue. The triangular head is edged with yellow and is of a darker green than the body. The white spiracles are surrounded by a pink area and the legs also have a pink tinge.

The Pupa. The Eyed Hawk burrows a couple of inches below the surface of the ground before pupating in a cell hollowed out by the wriggling caterpillar. In this underground chamber the larva remains for a week or a little longer, gradually shrinking in size, until the larval skin is cast. At first the pupa is a clear green, but it quickly darkens to a rich dark brown, verging on black. The surface is smooth and glossy and the shape cylindrical, tapering rather sharply towards the tail end and the short spine. It normally measures just over $3\frac{1}{2}$ cm in length and only slightly less in girth.

The Adult Moth. The Eyed Hawk is distinctive and easily recognized. When at rest the fore-wings, which are pinkish-grey, marbled and blotched with rich plum-brown, cover the rosy pink hind-wings which bear the characteristic eye-spot. This is a vivid violet-blue, darker in the centre, and is surrounded by a black ring. If the moth is disturbed it immediately raises the fore-wings so that these spots are revealed. The pinkish-grey thorax is marked with a large dark brown patch and the rest of the body is a soft grey-brown. The antennae are pale cream. On the underside the wings are pinkish-brown, banded with wavy lines of a paler pink and brown. The basal area of the fore-wings is a rich rosy red. The underside of the body is chocolate brown.

The Eyed Hawk used to be known as the Eyed Willow Hawk-moth, but this name is now no longer used and was, in any case, not strictly correct as the moth feeds, in the larval stage, on several other plants besides willow. Undoubtedly the favourite food of the larvae in the wild is willow or sallow (*Salix*) and there are a great many different varieties on which they have been found. Possibly the large-leaved sallow, *Salix caprea*, is the most common food plant. In gardens and orchards the larvae are discovered fairly frequently feeding on apple trees. I have found that large-leaved varieties, such as Bramley seedling, are preferred and my attempts at rearing larvae on the rather small-leaved Cox's Orange Pippin have always failed. In 1951 the caterpillars were reported to be so numerous in an orchard at Hawkhurst, in Kent, that they seriously defoliated the young apple trees.

Larvae feeding on apple seem to grow more slowly than those on sallow or willow. Compared to other hawk-moths they do grow rather slowly, specially in the early stages, and they seem to consume a greater quantity of food before reaching their full size than either Poplar Hawks

×10   ×10

The Eyed Hawk-moth lays its oval eggs on the undersides of the leaves. The young caterpillar begins to feed at the tip of a leaf, rests between meals in a typical attitude along the mid-rib and grows steadily, casting its skin four times. Finally it makes its way underground and turns into a thick, glossy pupa. The beautiful moth emerges the following spring and climbs up the nearest support to dry its wings.

×4

×10

×1

×3/4

×1¼

21

or Lime Hawks. The greeny-white colouring which is characteristic in all stages is more marked when they are feeding on sallow or willow leaves than when they are feeding on apple.

In the young stages the caterpillars eat the leaves but leave the central rib and cling to this while resting. From the second instar onwards they assume the sphinx attitude when not feeding, clinging on only with the claspers and last two pairs of pro-legs and curving the rest of the body downwards or outwards, away from their support. The blue colouring on the tail horn does not appear until the last instar. During the earlier stages it is at first pale pink and then purplish on the upper surface, but quite pale beneath. Throughout its development the caterpillar is of a more or less even thickness, without any swellings or bumps on its body. The head, which at first seems rather large, has two points on the crown but these disappear in the last stage. Occasionally larvae are found with rather indistinct red spots along the sides. Before pupating the caterpillar undergoes a slight colour change. The clear whitish-green becomes suffused with a dull buff yellow, and when the caterpillar is handled it twitches violently from side to side, bending its body until the head almost touches the tail. The reason for these convulsive movements is not clear, but they may be a form of defence to frighten insect-eating birds which might attack the larvae after they have left their feeding places and are making their way to earth to pupate.

Eyed Hawk larvae often wander a long way before they begin to burrow and this interval between feeding and 'going down' is a time of great danger, for unless the caterpillar is crawling between tussocks of grass it may easily be spotted by some predatory bird. Once a suitable place has been found, with soft friable earth, the larva will soon burrow out of sight and by wriggling and twisting it will hollow out and solidify an underground chamber to protect the pupa, which is more fragile and easily injured than that of the Poplar and Lime Hawks. Unfortunately a great many Eyed Hawk larvae and eggs become parasitized in the wild.

The moth emerges late in May or during the early part of June, but late specimens may continue to appear until the end of June. The emergence usually takes place early in the morning and unless the moth has settled in some very ill-chosen spot such as on the wall of a house, it is not likely to be noticed. Usually, in nature, it hangs by its feet from some slender twig and the brown mottled fore-wings, with their wavy edges, held on either side of the curved body, make the insect look so much like a bunch of crumpled dead leaves that only a trained naturalist who knows what he is looking for would immediately recognize the moth.

At the slightest touch, however, the Eyed Hawk gives itself away, at least to humans, by revealing its false eyes, the glaring black-ringed spots on the rich pink hind-wings. At the same time as the fore-wings are raised to expose the spots, the body is hunched up in a curious manner and the wings are moved forward, so that the brown thorax and abdomen become more prominent and take on a likeness to a nose or perhaps a beak between the glaring eyes. This is undoubtedly a device for frightening insect-eating birds which might accidentally have pecked at the moth while hunting around for food among the leaves.

An interesting experiment to prove this was performed by the German entomologist Standfuss. He had, in a cage, several captive birds, including a black-cap, a nightingale and a pair of robins and then introduced some Lime Hawks and Eyed Hawks to test their reactions. The birds immediately attacked the Lime Hawks and devoured them, after first pecking them to pieces, but when they touched the Eyed Hawk and the insect at once displayed its eye-spots, the birds were obviously frightened and flew away to the far side of the cage, flapping anxiously as if trying to escape. Neither the black-cap nor the robins dared to attack the insect a second time, but the nightingale, which had been captive for a number of years and was used to being offered all kinds of insects, including quite large spiders and butterflies, eventually overcame its fear, killed the moth and ate it.

More recently Dr Niko Tinbergen has carried out similar experiments with jays, and even these large and aggressive birds are frightened when the moth displays its eye-spots. I well remember being invited to visit the research station where he was working near Oxford, to see how some of the living insect material I had supplied was being used. We cycled out from the town to a private wood where a fairly large area had been enclosed with wire netting to form a natural aviary. A young Dutchman was in charge of the experiments and at that time tests were being made to ascertain how well protected hawk-moth caterpillars were by their natural camouflage, and it was obvious that if the caterpillars were sitting in their natural upside-down position, they were much better protected than if they were placed the wrong way round.

The Eyed Hawk does not become active until the evening and generally begins to fly a little later than the Poplar and the Lime Hawk, when it is almost dark. The males assemble to the virgin females and the pairs remain in copula for a full twenty-four hours. The female lays her total complement of eggs within the next few nights, scattering them widely over a large area.

These moths seldom vary in appearance but occasionally specimens are found with the hind-wing colour much lighter, or alternatively richer than usual, and I have also bred an insect without any eye-spots at all. Sometimes the hind-wings are yellowish, and now and then specimens are found with a much deeper and richer brown colouring than normal.

The Poplar Hawk

LAOTHOE POPULI

Haunts. The Poplar Hawk is the most common and widely distributed of all the European hawk-moths. It is found all over northern and central Europe, especially in France where poplar trees are such a feature of the landscape, and it also occurs in Russia, Scandinavia and Finland. In Great Britain it is widespread and common in suitable localities, including Scotland and Ireland, and it is even found in the Shetlands. Its main haunts are naturally in rather low-lying areas where a high water table favours the growth of poplars, sallows and willows.

The Egg. The Poplar Hawk lays a large, almost round, pale green egg, measuring about 1·9 mm across. It appears quite smooth, but under a magnifying glass fine reticulations can be seen on the surface. A fertile female will lay about two hundred eggs, fixing them singly or in groups of two or three on the leaves, where they can be found without much difficulty, even on low twigs and saplings. The time of incubation varies with the temperature and may be anything from ten to twenty days.

The Caterpillar. The young larvae, which usually eat part of the egg shells after hatching, are pale green with a cream-coloured horn. After only a few days the roughness of their skins becomes apparent. The full-fed caterpillars are stout and very solid in appearance. The most usual colour is a clear, somewhat yellowish green, thickly marked with tiny raised yellow dots. Seven oblique yellow lines, the first and the last being much brighter than the rest, decorate the sides of the body, and the last one extends into the tail horn which is now dark at the tip. The head has a yellow edge and is somewhat pinkish on the crown. The spiracles are pink and the legs are marked with pinkish-brown. Another less common form of the caterpillar is blue-green with much less noticeable cream-coloured dots and occasionally individuals are found with a row of light crimson spots along each side of the body. The larvae develop rather unevenly, some reaching their full size much sooner than others. The number of moults also varies, and may be either three or four.

The Pupa.   The fully fed larva burrows a couple of inches below the surface of the ground and there changes into a pupa without spinning any kind of cocoon. The pupa is very dark in colour, often almost black, dull and rather rough to the touch. It is very thick and solid, measuring about $3\frac{1}{2}$ cm in length and over 4 cm in girth. The wingcases are short and the body ends in a rough, flattened spine, with two rounded rough bumps immediately beneath it.

The Adult Moth.   The imago generally emerges during the night or very early in the morning. Although the Poplar Hawk is not at all colourful, the prominent yellowish-red veining and the delicate shading of the grey scalloped wings, decorated with darker bands, makes it a very attractive insect. When the fore-wings are raised, the rust-red patch at the base of the hind-wings is revealed. The thorax is covered with long grey silky hairs, the antennae are almost white and the abdomen plain grey. The fore-wings are marked with a distinct cream-coloured spot. On the underside the wings are a light grey-brown, faintly banded with darker lines and the fore-wings are rather paler towards the base. The females have much stouter, straighter bodies than the males and are usually a good deal larger and lighter in colour. A specimen of average size will measure just under 10 cm in wing-span, but there is always a wide variation between individuals, both those caught in the wild and specimens bred in captivity.

It is usually quite easy to recognize a Poplar Hawk caterpillar in all stages because of its stocky appearance. When young, the larvae sit along the veins on the undersides of the leaves, but after the second moult they assume a different and very characteristic attitude, hanging downwards from a leaf or stalk, holding on with their sucker feet and claspers, or sometimes even with the claspers only and curving the head inwards so that they have a humped look. Often, when they have eaten part of a leaf they will cling to the edge of the remainder filling up the empty space with their plump green bodies.

They will feed on all kinds of poplars as well as on willow, sallow and aspen. They have also been recorded on alder, birch and laurustinus, but this is rare. A fully fed larva measures about $6\frac{1}{2}$ cm in length. The colour change before pupation is only very slight, and can best be described as a general all-over dulling of the green colour, which takes on a dirty, greyish look. The caterpillars shrink and become very firm to the touch and often take up a position with the body sharply curved to one side. Under unnaturally crowded conditions they will sometimes eat each other's tail horns but this does not seem to affect the development of the moth in any way.

The Poplar Hawk is not usually content to pupate among surface rubbish, but actually burrows down into the soil where the dark pupa, almost the same colour as the soil and quite without any gloss to give it away, is well protected even if the ground is disturbed by scratching animals. The larvae usually pupate quite close to the base of the trees where they have been feeding and in the spring the moths crawl up the grey trunks to expand their wings. When at rest, in a normal position, the Poplar Hawk carries its wings on either side of the body, the

The Poplar Hawk caterpillar is very compact and stocky in appearance. Its skin is covered in tiny raised dots which give it a rough texture.

$\times 1\frac{1}{2}$

27

fore-wings sloping down at an angle so that the front edge and part of the outer margin of the hind-wings is visible above them. The antennae are folded down on either side of the thorax and the two front pairs of legs are stretched forward. In the male, the body has a characteristic strong upward curve at the tip. The moth very seldom takes to the wing in daylight, even if disturbed, and can easily be picked up when found. The mated pairs can also be handled without separating, as long as this is done gently and carefully.

The moths begin to emerge during May and occasionally, in a very warm spring, specimens have been caught at the end of April; and late moths are often on the wing late in June or even at the beginning of July. On the Continent a second brood appears regularly in August but in Britain only a small proportion of the pupae emerge the same season, the majority lying over until the spring. Larvae have been found as late as September and in a mild autumn they are able to complete their metamorphosis before the leaves fall. Occasionally out of season moths are recorded and in late January 1922 a female was taken at light near Shooters Hill in south-east London. In 1884 a contributor to *The Entomologist* claimed to have reared three generations in one season, by keeping the insects in a warm greenhouse to speed their development.

Like the Lime Hawk, the Poplar Hawk begins to fly at dusk and the males assemble to the waiting females. The flight is powerful and rather noisy but fairly slow and lumbering. The moths often appear at lighted windows or in mercury vapour moth traps. After mating the pairs remain together for twenty-four hours in the same attitude as Lime Hawks. Very soon after they separate the following evening the female begins to lay.

The Poplar Hawk is nothing like as variable as the Lime Hawk, but several distinct colour forms do occur. Especially in the females a decided pink overall shading is not uncommon and sometimes there may be an almost purplish tinge on the wings. Very pale grey, or practically creamy-coloured forms are also found, as well as individuals which are much darker than normal. Dark forms are common in Scotland. The size of the red area on the hind-wings may also vary and specimens have been found with very little red at all, while in others the patch of colour is greatly extended.

Halved gynandromorphs have been caught or bred on many occasions and when the female half is of the pink type, this aberration is very striking, the body being clearly divided into two halves, one pinkish and the other grey. In the majority of cases the right side is male and the left side female. My father, who was an exceptionally clever breeder of insects, used to examine his entire stock of Poplar Hawk pupae each autumn, picking out those which would produce gynandromorphs, by looking at the shape of the antennae, that on the male side being thicker than the female side. By touching the pupa with a wetted finger, the outline of the antennae could more easily be distinguished, and all abnormal pupae were set aside. He discovered, when breeding large numbers, that a tendency to this abnormality of mixed sexes was inherited in certain strains of the moth, and by introducing 'pink' blood he succeeded in breeding several very fine specimens with a strong colour contrast between the male and the female half of the body.

The Elephant Hawk

DEILEPHILA ELPENOR

Haunts. This moth is found generally all over Europe, including the British Isles, and also occurs in Scandinavia and Finland. It is, mainly, a lowland insect, inhabiting especially river valleys, but it is found also in forest clearings, railway cuttings and on wasteland, wherever the rosebay willowherb (*Epilobium*) grows. At the end of the war and for some years afterwards, it was common on bomb sites in London and other large cities, where willowherb, or 'fire weed', had sprung up among the ruins. It is attracted to light and consequently will come to windows at night and is often caught in mercury vapour moth traps.

The Egg. The pale green, round eggs are laid in June, singly, or sometimes in twos or threes on the undersides of the leaves both on the common rosebay willowherb (*Epilobium angustifolium*), the great hairy willowherb (*E. hirsutum*), the small willowherb (*E. parvifolium*) or on bedstraw (*Galium verum*). Occasionally the moth will lay in gardens on fuchsias or on evening primrose (*Oenothera*). Enchanter's nightshade (*Circaea luteiana*) sometimes serves as a food plant and there is even one record of larvae being found on bog-bean (*Menyanthes trifoliata*), and another on bindweed (*Convolvulus sepium*). The eggs hatch in ten to fifteen days, depending upon weather conditions.

The Caterpillar. The fully fed caterpillar measures 7 cm in length and occurs in two distinct colour forms—green and dark brown. The former is rare and although all the larvae are green during the first two instars, only about one per cent remain so until they pupate. The full-grown green larva is strikingly handsome, mottled with black patches on the back, especially on the front part of the body. The prominent eye-spots on the fifth and sixth segments, with creamy-white half-moon shaped corneas and black pupils, show up more vividly than they do in the brown form of the caterpillar. This typical form is sepia-brown, reticulated with black on the upper surface, while along the sides the colour

*The Elephant Hawk-moth has huge eyes and
slender, pale antennae.*

shades into a dull buff-yellow, which is especially marked on the fourth, fifth and sixth segments and at the joints. The legs are buff-yellow and the spiracles are the same colour, edged with black. The head is black and unusually small and the first three segments are very thin. The black tail horn is short and rather inconspicuous. The larvae begin to pupate about a month after hatching from the egg.

The Pupa. The Elephant Hawk pupates on the surface of the ground, in a rough cocoon fashioned from dead leaves, moss and debris, spun quite firmly together with silk threads. The pupa measures $3\frac{1}{2}$ to 4 cm in length and about $3\frac{1}{2}$ cm in girth. The colour is different from the other British hawk-moths, being a rather dull buff-brown with very dark brown markings. The wingcases are quite smooth, but the rest of the pupal shell is slightly rough to the touch, with short protruding points round the three segments below the wingcases. A characteristic of the Elephant Hawk is the great mobility of the pupa. From the time of pupation right until a few days before emergence, a healthy pupa will wriggle violently when touched. Before emerging the pupae often work their way half-way out of the cocoons by this wriggling movement.

The Adult Moth. The Elephant Hawk is the most beautiful of all the European hawk-moths. With fully extended wings it measures $7\frac{1}{2}$ cm from tip to tip. When freshly emerged, the dominant colour is a rich crimson-pink, contrasting with bands of bronzy-green. The pale antennae and legs and the white fringes on the wings and at the joint between the

31

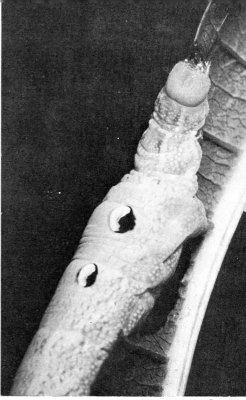

*The caterpillars of the Elephant Hawk-moth are
smooth and velvety to the touch. They feed
voraciously on willowherb and are decorated
with prominent eye-spots.*

wings and the body, contrasting with the crimson and green, give the
moth a unique air of elegance. The body is slim and pointed and when
at rest the insect holds its wings in such a way that its outline resembles
an arrow head. The underside is predominantly crimson.

The question which first comes to mind when considering the
Elephant Hawk is why a moth, of slender build and vivid colouring,
should have been given this name. The answer lies not in any feature
of the moth itself, but in the caterpillar, whose small head and unusually
slender anterior segments provide the clue. The name 'elephant' was
chosen for this caterpillar by the seventeenth-century Dutch entomologist Jan Goedart, who, in his book *Metamorphosis et Historia Naturae
Insectorum* published in 1662, gave his reason for choosing it: 'since it
has a thing in front of its head which is not at all a bad resemblance to
an elephant's trunk'. Certainly, when the larva is questing around for
food, with the front segments stretched to their limit and the body
waving to and fro, the likeness to a trunk is very striking, both in shape,
colouring and action.

32

When first hatched the caterpillar does not have this curious characteristic, but resembles almost any other typical hawk-moth larva, being light green and of even thickness, with a narrow, spine-like horn at the end of its body. After the first moult the smallness of the head becomes noticeable, and in the third instar, when the majority of the larvae have changed from green to brown, the proboscis effect is established. At this stage too, the eye-spots on the swollen fifth and sixth segments become noticeable, and when the larva is alarmed and retracts its head and puffs these segments up to more than their normal size, this part of the body looks so much like a rounded head with staring eyes that the true head is apt to be overlooked.

The four eye-spots, which are more startling in the green than in the brown form of the caterpillar, must, one assumes, have some protective function, by discouraging enemies from attacking the caterpillars. But as the larvae always hide low down among the herbage during the day, once they have reached this stage of development, and only crawl up the plants to feed at dusk, it is difficult to understand just what their use may be. That they do have enemies which attack and eat them in spite of the eye-spots is obvious. In the summer of 1963, having bred a number of Elephant Hawks in captivity, I had a large surplus of larvae which I released in a thicket of willowherb growing in a damp meadow. I did not actually count the larvae, which were in the third instar, but there must have been at least seven or eight hundred. And yet, when a fortnight later I visited the locality again, there was not one larva to be found, nor any sign of their feeding, and I came to the conclusion that they must have been eaten either by shrews, hedgehogs, birds or possibly toads.

On another occasion I made an experiment with my cat, a rather timid female, but a keen hunter. I placed half a dozen fully fed Elephant Hawk caterpillars on the paved terrace where she was sitting and they soon began to move towards her. With the curiosity of all feline animals she watched them closely, but did not try to spring, although her tail was swinging from side to side. Then, as the larvae approached, she moved forward to sniff at the leader, and the moment her whiskers touched its sensitive skin the caterpillar stopped, bunched itself up and distended the eye-spots. The cat jumped back, startled, and then retreated and would have nothing more to do with them. Whether this was due to the effect of the eye-spots or merely a revulsion against their scent (not apparent to a human nose, but possibly unpleasant to a cat) it was impossible to tell. Professor Poulton, the originator of the theory of mimicry, wrote that the Elephant Hawk caterpillar frightens away enemies 'by the suggestion of a cobra-like serpent' but this seems rather far-fetched in an insect which has no geographical connection with cobras whatsoever.

In its early green stages the caterpillar is extremely well camouflaged, being the exact shade of the willowherb leaves; hiding, as it does, on the under surface, sitting lengthways along the mid-rib of the leaf, it is almost invisible. The first brown skin, the colour of milk chocolate, slightly reticulated with darker lines, blends very well with the withered leaves which usually hang on the lower parts of the plants. The final very dark colouring is again more conspicuous unless the caterpillar is actually on the ground below the plants, where moist black earth and rubbish give it a suitable background.

A rather curious thing about the caterpillar of the Elephant Hawk is its behaviour in water, which was noted by Eleazar Albin, the artist and naturalist who published his illustrated book *A Natural History of English Insects* in 1720. As it often feeds on willowherb close to the water's side, or even overhanging a stream, it is not unusual for the caterpillar to drop accidentally into the water; but instead of sinking helplessly to the bottom it floats, wriggling violently, and by its contortions, which Albin described as 'swimming with head and tail turned together', often succeeds in making its way to the bank, where it can clutch at trailing plants and so gain dry land once more.

In the summer of 1941, six Elephant Hawk caterpillars were found at Windermere, feeding on bog-bean growing in a small garden pool. They crawled about among the partially submerged leaves and did not appear to mind getting wet. When three-parts grown they were put into glass jars and fed there on bog-bean leaves only, until they pupated. Two of the pupae which were kept as an experiment produced perfectly normal healthy adult moths the following summer. A very old record in *The Entomologist*, dating from 1873, describes how two Elephant caterpillars, mistaken for leeches, were transported for several miles in a jar of water, without coming to any harm.

The Elephant Hawk caterpillar is always rather sluggish in its movements and from what I have observed when rearing it in captivity, it does not seem to have the same strong desire to wander in search of a suitable pupating site, as some of the other hawk-moths. Possibly the fact that it does not have to find a patch of soft soil to burrow down into has something to do with it, as any accumulation of surface rubbish, dry grass or moss and dead leaves provides suitable material for the construction of the cocoon. The larva does not change colour prior to pupation, but merely shrinks a little and becomes more compact and firmer to the touch. The velvety softness of the skin, which is so characteristic, remains the same until the end of the larval life. The bi-coloured pupa cannot be confused with any other of the hawks, as it is considerably larger than that of the Small Elephant, which it most closely resembles in colouring.

The adult moth emerges from early to mid-June, depending on the season, and may still be on the wing at midsummer if the weather is cool. It never moves during the day, but hides away in some shady place among the leaves where it cannot easily be seen, and does not begin to fly until after sunset. Both sexes, which are almost identical in appearance, like to visit flowers such as valerian, honeysuckle or the early-flowering weeping buddleia and while feeding they hover in front of the blooms, probing with their long tongues for nectar.

The mating flight takes place soon after dark, but unlike the Poplar and Lime Hawks, which mate at dusk and remain paired until the following evening, the Elephant does not pair until nearly midnight and the couples do not remain in copula for very long, probably not more than two hours. The female begins to lay as soon as they have parted and continues to do so each night, for four or five days. In one particular case, observed in a breeding cage, a female laid eight eggs on the night of mating, a dozen the second night and thirty on the third night before being released. The total number of eggs may exceed a hundred if the moth finds sufficient food, and they are scattered over a wide area.

A young entomologist told me an extraordinary story of a female Elephant Hawk-moth, one of a brood that was bred in a garden shed. He went in to feed the moths at dusk carrying a saucer of sugar-water which he was going to sprinkle over a bunch of valerian flowers. The moths were already on the wing and as he approached the flowers they hovered round his hands and began to feed on the sweet liquid dripping from his fingers. Then, to his surprise, one of the moths actually alighted on his hand and began to lay eggs all over his fingers and palm. Altogether she laid eight eggs, which he removed carefully with the aid of a razor blade, and in due course they all hatched and he successfully reared the caterpillars to the pupal stage. This is just one example of the curious way moths can sometimes behave when bred under unnatural conditions in captivity.

The Elephant Hawk-moth is not a variable insect, although specimens with abnormal colouring occur from time to time, including very dark, melanic forms.

The Small Elephant Hawk

DEILEPHILA PORCELLUS

Haunts.   The Small Elephant Hawk is found throughout the Palearctic region and is common over most of Europe including the British Isles and the southern half of Sweden and Finland. It is an insect of the open meadowland or heath and is particularly abundant in chalk and lime-stone districts wherever its food plants are to be found. It also occurs on shingle beaches and sandhills along the coast.

The Egg.   The egg is oval in shape and rather small, measuring only 1 mm in width and a little more in length. It is clear green in colour and somewhat dented in on the upper surface. The eggs are fixed singly on the leaves while the moth hovers over the food plant. Usually they are laid on lady's bedstraw (*Galium verum*) or on other species of the same genus, but larvae have also been found on various willowherbs as well as on purple loosestrife (*Lythrum salicaria*) and even on grape-vine. In 1941 several larvae were found at Herne Bay in Kent feeding on *Genista tinctoria*. The egg turns a yellowish green before hatching and incubation takes from seven to fifteen days.

The Caterpillar.   When hatching, the caterpillar is no more than 3 mm long. Unlike all our other native hawk-moths it has no tail horn, but only a small double tubercle bearing two bristly hairs. The fully fed larva resembles that of the Large Elephant Hawk but it is much smaller in size, completely lacks a horn, and is of a more ashy colour, marked with black. The colouring on the lower portions of the front segments is pale buff. The fifth and sixth segments bear lilac-coloured eye-spots with brown centres. The underside of the body is paler than the back, with a slight pinkish tinge. As in the Large Elephant Hawk there is also a green form of the caterpillar. The ground colour is a soft light green, freckled on the back with transverse lines of fine black dots. A rather indistinct stripe runs along either side of the body and the eye-spots are a vivid rosy-mauve. When stretched out to its full extent, the caterpillar measures 5½ cm, but when at rest, with the head retracted, it is a centimetre shorter. Like its close relation it can extend the first four segments like a snout or a trunk while it is feeding, and in the hunched resting position the eye-spots become distended.

The Pupa. The Small Elephant Hawk larva does not burrow into the ground, but spins a loose cocoon on the surface, binding together leaves and pieces of rubbish with fine silk threads. The pupa measures only 3 cm in length and is rather slender. The eyes are prominent and the mouth parts are contained in a keel-like projection. At the tip of the abdomen is a triangular spike, which is slightly bent towards the underside. The three segments below the wingcases each have a ring of small sharp points. The skin of the pupa is dull and slightly rough, light brown in colour and marked on the wingcases and on the head with very dark brown. Each of the abdominal segments is also banded with dark brown.

The Adult Moth. The moth is quite small, measuring only about 5 cm in wing-span and less than half this in length of body. The wings are patterned in crimson and a dull ochreous yellow. The hind-wings are black at the base, yellowish in the centre and have a pink stripe along the margin. The body is crimson with white marks and spots on the abdomen and the legs and antennae are creamy-white. The body tapers rather suddenly to an elongated point. The colouring on the underside is also in crimson and yellow.

In scientific terminology the Small Elephant Hawk is 'the little pig', this being the literal translation of its specific name *porcellus*. This undoubtedly refers to the elongated 'snout' of the larva and is, I think, better than the comparison to an elephant's trunk.

Searching for the eggs of this moth in the wild is seldom very successful unless one has actually seen a female hovering and laying on a clump of bedstraw. It is, however, comparatively easy to find the larvae with the aid of a torch, when they are almost full grown, because they crawl up to the tops of the plants at night to feed, and retire again to their hiding places on the ground before the morning. I have done this several times on Dartford Heath in Kent with great success.

In captivity I have noticed that the newly hatched caterpillars like to begin by nibbling at the flowers, but after the first skin change they generally feed only on the leaves. The larvae are at first a very pale grey-green on the back and a more yellow-green on the underside of the body. After moulting the colour deepens and a whitish stripe appears along either side. After the second moult the characteristic 'snout' becomes apparent but the colour remains green and the wart which replaces the horn turns pink. After the third skin casting the majority of the larvae are still green, but darker colouring begins to appear and the eye-spots develop. In the last skin most of the larvae turn grey-brown. Only a very small percentage remain green until they pupate.

The Small Elephant Hawk is usually on the wing some time before its larger relation, at the beginning of June or even in May. There are also several records of the moth being found as late as July in years when the early summer has been unusually cool. This pretty little moth is often seen feeding from flowers and appears to be specially fond of rhododendrons and valerian. It also visits campion and viper's bugloss in the wild and has often been taken at sugar. An amusing old record tells of a Small Elephant 'rushing like a hawk' at the paint brush dipped in sugar solution which a collector had just taken out of the pot to sugar a tree trunk. It must have been an exceptionally hungry moth to be so bold. It has been noticed that the moths begin to arrive for food at about 8 p.m. and continue flying until 10.30 p.m. A powerful light will attract them and a mercury vapour moth trap has been known to capture as many as forty specimens in a night. Generally, however, the Small Elephant Hawk is not very abundant anywhere, although it is widely distributed. In southern Europe there is often a partial second brood, but in England the moth produces only one generation a year. The moths are seldom seen paired, but there is one record of a pair found in copula at 1.30 a.m. on a tall stalk of grass.

The Small Elephant Hawk is a rather variable moth and many aberrations have been caught or bred in which the proportion of yellow and crimson on the wings varies from the normal, or the markings have become indistinct and blurred. Sometimes the pink colouring may be replaced by grey or the yellow may be of a greenish tint. Variation in the depth and tone of both the pink and yellow colouring also occurs. Specimens from Scotland often have a more greenish ground colour than normal, with very distinct markings while those from western Ireland are more yellow.

The Broad-bordered Bee Hawk

HEMARIS FUCIFORMIS

Haunts. This is a woodland insect flying in sunny glades and ridings, or along the edges of woods where honeysuckle twines among the shrubs. It is generally a rather local moth but often quite common in regions where it does occur. It is found over most of Europe, including the Scandinavian countries. In Britain it is confined more or less to the southern half of the country and does not occur either in Scotland or in Ireland.

The Egg. The almost round, green eggs measure just over 1 mm across and are fixed, singly, on the underside of honeysuckle leaves while the moth is on the wing. In places where these insects are common the eggs can easily be found by searching the sprays. They are deposited in late May and early June. Occasionally the moth lays on snowberry (*Symphoricarpus*) or on bedstraw (*Galium*) as well as on honeysuckle (*Lonicera periclymenum*). The eggs hatch in about a fortnight.

The Caterpillar. The fully fed caterpillar is $3\frac{1}{2}$ cm long, with a body which tapers from the rather stout middle section towards the head and tail. The horn is curved, lilac-coloured at the base, purplish-brown in the middle and dark brown at the tip. The general ground colour of the body is a bright green with a whitish tinge along the back. The head is blue-green and an interrupted green line runs along the centre of the back. There is a faint yellowish line along each side, ending at the horn. The underside of the body is reddish-brown, edged with a yellow line. The spiracles are surrounded by patches of the same reddish colour, which vary somewhat in size and shape.

The Pupa. The pupa is enclosed in a flimsy cocoon made from silk of a dirty pink colour, interwoven with fragments of leaf, earth, moss and other rubbish. It is $2\frac{1}{2}$ cm in length, rather slender, broadest across the wingcases and tapering towards the head and tail, which is furnished with a sharp triangular spike. The surface of the pupa is slightly glossy and a dark, rich brown, with black bands on the abdominal segments and black markings on the wingcases.

The Adult Moth. The Broad-bordered Bee Hawk is quite a small moth, measuring not much more than 4–4½ cm in wing-span. When the insect first emerges the wings have a cloudy look because they are still covered with a thin layer of light brown scales, but these quickly fall away, leaving the wings transparent, except for the border round the edges. Along the front margin this is quite narrow and dark brown while the outer margin of both pairs of wings has a fairly broad rich reddish-brown border of scales. The nervures in the transparent area are a dark reddish-black and the base of the wings has the same colour, extending along the inner margin. The end of the discoidal cell on the fore-wing is marked with a short oblique line of the same colour. The antennae are black and very thick towards the tip, with a short, bent bristle. They are very slightly thicker in the male than in the female, but otherwise the sexes are alike. The head and thorax are covered in dull yellow fur and the abdomen has a broad reddish-brown band round the middle. The segments behind the band are dull yellow with paler yellow side tufts and the tip of the body is decorated with a prominent tuft of hairs, yellow in the centre and black on either side. On the under surface the front edge and the base of the wings is clear yellow. The marginal band is rusty red and the entire surface of the wings has an iridescent purple sheen, which is also noticeable on the upper side. The underside of the thorax is clothed with pale yellow hair, the abdomen is reddish-brown and yellow and the tail tuft black.

This rather curious little moth appears to mimic a bumble bee. It is diurnal, flying only in daylight, and is usually most active before noon, settling for periods of rest after midday. It is particularly fond of visiting the flowers of rhododendrons and azaleas but it is also often seen hovering over smaller plants such as bugle (*Ajuga reptans*), ragged robin (*Lychnis flos-cuculi*) and yellow rattle (*Rhinantus crista-galli*). It is shy and easily frightened, and any sudden movement nearby will cause it to disappear with great speed. It usually appears on the wing towards the end of May and continues to fly for about three weeks. Both pairing and egg-laying take place during the day.

When feeding, the caterpillars nibble round holes through the honeysuckle leaves on either side of the mid-rib, and this habit makes it comparatively easy to find them, even when they are quite small. When first hatched they are whitish-yellow, but soon assume a green

×2

*The Broad-bordered Bee Hawk-moth has
transparent wings surrounded by a border of
reddish-brown scales, and its body bears tufts
of coloured fur.*

colouring. Until the last instar the skin is rough and covered in small raised whitish spots, but when the caterpillar is full grown the skin is quite smooth.

The larvae vary to some extent in appearance but the ground colour is always green. Sometimes there is a row of crescent-shaped reddish spots along each side, as well as the red areas round the spiracles. Shortly before pupating the caterpillar turns a dull reddish-brown, darker on the back than on the under surface. It is then very difficult to detect among debris on the ground. In captivity larvae have been reared on various kinds of cultivated honeysuckle and also on snowberry, but in the wild they always prefer the common honeysuckle. In southern Europe and in the lower alpine valleys the moth is double brooded, but elsewhere only a single brood appears each season.

The Narrow-bordered Bee Hawk

HEMARIS TITYUS

Haunts. This moth has a wide distribution, being found throughout Europe, ranging northwards to Scotland and Lapland and westwards to Ireland where it is very common in many different localities. It is an insect of meadow land and open woodland glades, where in May and June the moths can be seen eagerly feeding from flowers on warm sunny days. In England it is rather more common in the north and west than in the southern counties.

The Egg. The green spherical eggs are laid singly, normally on leaves of the devil's-bit scabious (*Scabiosa succisa*), but also on field scabious (*Scabiosa arvensis*), and larvae have been recorded on the cultivated garden scabious (*Scabiosa caucasica*). The time of hatching varies from a week to a fortnight, depending on the weather.

The Caterpillar. The fully fed caterpillar is the same size as that of the Broad-bordered Bee Hawk, but rather more slender, tapering gently from the sixth segment towards the head. The ground colour is green and varies in shade in different individuals, ranging from a very pale almost whitish-green to a dull blue-green, and the colouring is nearly always darker on the front of the body. The head is also green. A pale greenish-yellow, narrow line runs along each side and just above it, starting on the fifth segment, is a row of purplish-red, slightly elongated spots. From the fifth segment backwards the spiracles are surrounded by large pear-shaped spots of the same colour, each one edged with a narrow band of yellowish-green. The underside of the body and the horn, which is only slightly curved, are also reddish-purple. The skin is slightly rough and covered in tiny raised whitish dots. The size and number of spots varies to some extent in different specimens. Buff-coloured or purplish larvae have also been recorded.

The Pupa. The pupa is enclosed in a web of coarse silk and is either on the surface of the ground among rubbish or buried very shallowly.

42

× 1½

× 1½

The Privet Hawk-moth
Sphinx ligustri

*This fine, large moth
is a typical representative
of the hawk-moths, with
its narrow, pointed wings
and hovering flight. The
caterpillar assumes an
attitude reminiscent of an
Egyptian sphinx, except
that it always sits
upside down.*

$\times 1\frac{3}{4}$

$\times \frac{3}{4}$

The Pine Hawk-moth
Hyloicus pinastri

This is the only European hawk-moth whose caterpillar feeds on conifers. It is extremely well camouflaged in all its stages, blending with the bark or the pine needles amongst which it hides. At the present time the moth is rapidly extending its range in England.

$\times 1\frac{1}{2}$

$\times 2$

$\times \frac{3}{4}$

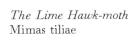

The Lime Hawk-moth
Mimas tiliae

*The Lime Hawk is the most variable
of all the hawk-moths, both in colour and
markings. The two spots on the fore-wings
are sometimes joined into a thick band,
sometimes reduced very much in size and
occasionally completely missing. There is
also a distinct colour difference between the
sexes. This is a female moth; the male is
predominantly green. The caterpillar
changes from a clear green to an
inconspicuous dusky hue just before it is
due to crawl down the tree trunk to pupate
in the soil.*

$\times 1\frac{1}{4}$

×1½

The Eyed Hawk-moth
Smerinthus ocellata

*This large moth is normally very well
camouflaged when at rest, and
experiments have shown that if it is
disturbed and reveals the startling blue
eye-spots, this has a frightening effect
on birds. The Eyed Hawk will
hybridize with the Poplar Hawk, and
the parents and their progeny are shown
here. The caterpillar has been
photographed in a characteristic attitude
on a twig of willow.*

×⅓

×½

The Poplar Hawk-moth
Laothoe populi

A mated pair clinging to the rough bark of a tree-trunk, the female is a pink variety, the male typically grey. The two photographs of the caterpillars show one newly hatched from the egg, the other almost fully grown.

×1¼

×5

×½

×2

The Elephant Hawk-moth
Deilephila elpenor

*Widely distributed in
Europe and Great Britain,
this moth is found mainly
in lowland districts where
rosebay willowherb grows.
It takes its name from
the caterpillar's habit of
stretching out the front
segments when questing
for food. When the
caterpillar retracts its
head, the false 'eyes' on
the fifth and sixth
segments have a startling
effect. Young larvae show
a great variety of
colouring.*

×1

×1

The Small Elephant Hawk-moth
Deilephila porcellus

*This elegant moth is not as
widely distributed as its larger
relation and is found in more
open, sunny terrain. It begins
to emerge some weeks earlier
and is very fond of visiting
rhododendron flowers. The
caterpillars usually feed on
lady's bedstraw, remaining
hidden at ground-level during
the day, and crawling up on the
stalks at night.*

$\times 1\frac{1}{4}$

×2

The Broad-bordered Bee Hawk
Hemaris fuciformis

This little hawk-moth might at first glance be mistaken for a bumble bee, but its fast, darting flight is very different. It is a woodland insect and the plump caterpillars feed on the leaves of wild honeysuckle. When the moth first emerges the wings are covered with scales, but these quickly drop off, leaving only a red-brown margin.

×1½

It measures only about 2½ cm in length and is rather slender, narrowing towards the head and tapering gently to the flat triangular tail spine which has its tip bent towards the under surface of the body. The skin of the pupa is somewhat rough and the colour a dark brownish-black, tinted with deep reddish-brown, especially at the joints of the abdominal segments and on the back of the thorax.

The Adult Moth. When freshly emerged the moth has a thin layer of greyish scales on its wings, but these fall off as soon as it begins to fly, leaving only a very narrow border of brownish-grey, which is widest near the apex of the fore-wings. The rest of the wings becomes glass clear, with dark brown nervures. When the light strikes the wing at a certain angle a purplish iridescence is visible. The antennae are long and dark, thickening towards the tip and end in a hooked bristle. The body is covered in thick fur which is yellowish-brown on the thorax. The abdomen is marked first with a broad dark brown band, followed by a band of dull orange with tufts of yellow hair on either side. The tip of the body is decorated with two brown tufts, separated by a few orange hairs. On the underside the body is dark grey with yellow patches on either side of the abdomen and the legs are clothed in greyish-yellow hairs. The base of the wings is tinted with yellow.

In general appearance the Narrow-bordered Bee Hawk so closely resembles a rather pale bumble bee, that it might easily be mistaken for one when it hovers in front of flowers, probing for nectar. Unlike a bumble bee, however, it does not actually settle on the blooms, nor does it make a loud buzzing noise and its flight is very quick and agile. No bumble bee can disappear as rapidly as a Bee Hawk when disturbed, and also, unlike its namesake, it is generally most active before midday; but it sometimes also flies in the early afternoon, especially on rather cloudy days, when its movements are not as rapid as in sunlight. This attractive little moth, with its softly furry body, has suffered some confusion in naming, having been known at various times as both *Macroglossa bombyliformis* and *M. fuciformis*, which has caused a great deal of confusion with its close relation the Broad-bordered Bee Hawk, which has also borne both names. It has now been classified in the genus *Hemaris* and has been given the specific name of *tityus* which is the original one selected by Linnaeus.

In Britain the moth is single-brooded, but in the southern parts of Europe, including Switzerland where it is common everywhere, it has a second brood in August. The eggs are laid on the undersides of the leaves, usually singly, and the most common food plant is devil's-bit

The caterpillar of the Narrow-bordered Bee Hawk is comparatively
small, although typical of the hawk-moths in shape. The colouring
is green with well-defined purplish-red spots.

scabious. The larvae reveal their presence by eating holes in the leaves, on either side of the mid-rib. They do not cling closely to the food plant like most hawk-moth larvae, but drop to the ground when disturbed and are then easily overlooked. I once found a small brood of caterpillars feeding on scabious on a piece of marshy ground near one of the famous lead lakes in the Mendips in Somerset. They have also been reported more than once on garden scabious and seem to prefer the leaves low down on the plants. There is practically no difference in appearance between the sexes and they are both the same size, measuring a little more than $4\frac{1}{2}$ cm in wing-span. Variations in colour or markings are practically unknown.

The Death's-head Hawk

ACHERONTIA ATROPOS

Haunts. This famous hawk-moth is distributed throughout Africa, western Asia, and most of Europe where it is a migrant, and at least a few specimens reach the British Isles every summer. Records over many years show that the immigrants tend to arrive here, usually from the beginning of June onwards, over the south-east coast. Quite a few have been picked up alive on beaches where they have obviously settled immediately on arrival under cover of darkness. During the last great 'Death's-head Year', which was in 1956, the moths were found all over the country from Folkestone to Inverness and from Devon to Northumberland. One was even picked up on the pavement in Victoria Street in London. They are attracted to lighted windows and by the scent of honey from bee-hives, and naturally to fields and allotments where potatoes grow, as the haulm is the main food of the caterpillars.

The Egg. The eggs, which are small for the size of the moth, are laid on the leaves of the food plant, generally singly. They are pale green in colour, oval in shape and measure only about $1\frac{1}{2}$ mm in length. Just before hatching they turn a golden-buff colour. There appears to be no record of an egg ever being found wild in this country.

The Caterpillar. The fully fed caterpillar is large and stout, almost cylindrical in shape and may measure as much as 12 or 13 cm in length. In the last instar there are several distinct colour forms. One of these is a clear apple green with seven sloping blue and yellow stripes on each side of the body, meeting on the back in V-shaped points. The back itself is sprinkled with small dots of deep Prussian blue. The front of the body is plain green and so is the head, which is decorated with a black band. The other common form is clear yellow with dark purple dots and the oblique stripes are blue on the back and purple further down the sides, each one with a narrow white edge. Two other variations are a greenish-yellow with dark-edged blue stripes and a yellow form

45

striped with blue and green. All these have a dark yellow tail horn which is rough in texture and bent downwards, with an upward curl at the tip. The spiracles are black and the front part of the body has a slightly swollen and semi-transparent look. There is also a brown form, in which the front segments may be whitish or a dull pink, while the diagonal stripes are replaced by a series of X-shaped marks along the back, while the tail is brown. In central Europe this dark form is rare, but becomes more common in the south, and in Africa green and brown caterpillars are equally common.

The Pupa. The Death's-head pupates underground, in a chamber hollowed out by the caterpillar. The pupa is a rich mahogany brown, $7\frac{1}{2}$ cm or more in length with a straight, sharp point at the tail. The females are slightly larger and heavier than the males. The pupa acquires a high gloss through constant wriggling and rubbing against the sides of the chamber and twitches vigorously when handled. Shortly before the moth emerges the pupa turns black and will squeak when touched.

The Adult Moth. The Death's-head is the largest and heaviest of the European hawk-moths, measuring 11 cm or more in wing-span, with a body length of 6 cm and a girth of about 4 cm round the abdomen. The wings are broad and rounded at the tip. The fore-wings are marbled in black and brown, with a distinct buff-coloured round discoidal spot and a short irregular band of the same colour running from the front margin half-way across the wing. The hind-wings are a rich deep yellow, decorated with two bands of black and with black lines running along the nervures to the edge. The head and thorax are covered in dense grey-black fur and on the thorax is a distinct dull yellow mark, very much resembling a human skull. The abdomen is banded in black and yellow with a grey-blue band running down the centre and becoming wider towards the tail end. There is a dark grey line along either side of the abdomen. The antennae are of medium length, thickening slightly towards the white tip which is furnished with a hooked black bristle. On the underside, both the wings and the body are yellow, banded with black. The dark eyes, which appear to glow at night, are unusually large. There is·a considerable individual variation in size and also in the shape of the wings as well as in the colour of the skull mark, which is often grey instead of ochreous yellow. Occasionally this characteristic feature is barely noticeable, having blended into the ground colour of the thorax. The bands on the hind-wings also vary, and so does the depth of the yellow colouring, both on the wings and on the abdomen, and the fore-wings may also be either much paler or darker than normal.

With folded wings, in its natural resting position, the Death's-head gives a sombre impression, as the black-banded yellow hind-wings are hidden. The curious skull-like mark on the thorax, in conjunction with the transverse black bars across the yellow body, reminding one of the ribs of a human skeleton, has been the cause of a great deal of superstition. Added to this the moth squeaks loudly, rather like a mouse or a creaky shoe. This noise is not produced by vocal chords but by the moth forcing air through a fissure at the base of its short tongue.

The very mention of the Death's-head Hawk-moth stirs the imagination of all naturalists because it is the largest and the most remarkable of the European moths. Its generic name, *Acherontia*, is taken from Acheron, a river in Hades, and alludes to the skull mark, the symbol of death, so boldly marked on the thorax. The specific name is also derived from classical mythology, *Atropos* being one of the Fates, the destroyers of life. It also links with *Atropa belladonna*, the deadly nightshade, on which the caterpillars sometimes feed.

Historians do not often concern themselves with insects, unless they are relating the frightening story of some plague or famine caused by fleas or locusts, but the French writer Jules Michelet was interested in the Death's-head moth which occurred in great numbers in France shortly before the revolution. He surmised that the caterpillars had been introduced with the potato some time earlier, but of course he was wrong. It is certain that the moth existed in Europe long before Sir Walter Raleigh brought potatoes from the West Indies and they became the most important food of the peasantry. In fact, I think it would be safe to say that this moth haunted Europe long before its human inhabitants were civilized. But like the populace, the caterpillars of the Death's-head quickly learnt to appreciate the food value of the new crop, even though they fed on the leaves and not on the tubers, and undoubtedly potato growing encouraged its spread. Previously the caterpillars had fed on jasmine and on wild plants of the nightshade family. Wilkes, the natural history writer in the eighteenth century, called it the Jasmine Hawk.

The European peasants, and especially the people in Brittany, did not like the Death's-head at all and their feelings had nothing to do with the caterpillars eating potato leaves. Their dislike was based entirely on the strange and rather macabre appearance of the moth. It became known as the 'Death's-head Phantom' or the 'Wandering Death Bird' and was regarded as an omen of death and disaster. I have discovered the

The splendid caterpillar of the
Death's-head is sometimes found
feeding on potato haulm in
gardens or on allotments.
The moth has a great liking for
honey and hungry migrants have
been discovered trying to enter
bee-hives. A modern hive is almost
proof against such marauders,
but the old-fashioned skep type had
a wider entrance so that the moths
could easily get in.

$\times \frac{3}{4}$

$\times \frac{3}{4}$

record of a letter to a Mr Knapp, written by a correspondent in German Poland in 1824, and I quote: 'The markings of the moth represent to their fertile imaginations the head of a perfect skeleton with the limb bones crossed beneath; its cry becomes the voice of anguish, the moaning of a child, the signal of grief; it is regarded not as the creation of a benevolent being, but as the device of evil spirits—spirits enemies to man, conceived and fabricated in the dark; the very shining of its eyes is thought to represent the fiery element, whence it is supposed to have proceeded. Flying into their apartments in the evening it at times extinguishes the light, foretelling war, pestilence, hunger and death to man and beast. In central France a belief prevails that the dust cast from its wings in flying through a room, produces blindness if it happens to fall upon the eyes.'

In more recent years a naturalist discovered in the Death's-head a likeness to a Dominican monk and after rearing two of these moths in captivity he wrote the following note to *The Entomologist*. 'I observed these interesting moths for some time alive, and the larger one, with the normal and very conspicuous "death's-head" on the thorax, gave me a surprise. Soon after the freshly emerged insects had dried their wings and settled themselves into the position common to most moths when at rest, I approached the cage which stood in an obscure corner, with the intention of studying the appearance of the specimens. The larger one was resting against the side of the cage, a dusky inconspicuous shape; the smaller moth was hanging on the roof with its head towards me and its very large eyes glowed like live coals in the half light.

'Looking closer at the grey uncertain form on the side wall of the cage, I was struck with its likeness to a hooded long-robed figure of a medieval monk, but with a naked bleached skull grinning out from the hood. With my head inside the breeding cage, I inadvertently disturbed the moth on the roof whereupon it uttered a series of sobbing squeaks, and then it suddenly seemed to me as if the white skull in the dark form on the side of the cage just before my face had become alive, and was nodding at me. The impression in the gloom was so weird and startling that I turned my head towards the light to see if my eyes were at fault but nothing evidently was the matter with them. Looking back at the moth I again saw the "skull" nodding horribly and both moths were now emitting their plaintive squeaks for which they are well known.

'Nothing remained but to fetch the lamp and to bring its light to bear on these twentieth century spectres. Immediately, then, it became plain that the white skull-like disc on the thorax was movable, and now palpitating rapidly, thus being under the above conditions capable of causing the impression of a head nodding out from a dark cowl.'

Curiously enough in Egypt, which is probably the home of most of the migrants flying northwards through Europe, this moth is affectionately known as 'the father of the family'. The origin of this rather curious name is obscure, but it may be based on a misunderstanding of its frequent presence in bee-hives. It does not enter from any paternal feeling, however, but simply because it can scent the honey through the sensitive nerve endings on its thick antennae and is attracted by the smell. Death's-heads have very often been seen flying around or crawling over bee-hives at dusk and although modern hives are almost impossible for such a bulky insect to enter, the old-fashioned skep type with a wide entrance was almost an invitation to the Death's-head. How the moths fared once they got inside is not easy to judge, but bee keepers through the centuries have been able to testify to many casualties. At one time it was thought that the squeak of the moth had a curious mesmeric effect on the bees, subduing their aggressiveness and leaving the lumbering visitors free to wander over the combs helping themselves unmolested to the stores. This is unlikely and observers have actually seen the moths being attacked by scores of furious bees and many dead moths have been found entombed in a covering of wax at the bottom of the hive.

The Danish naturalist Hoffmeyer has commented on the tongue of the Death's-head, which is short and thick and pointed at the tip, and in his opinion the moth is a specialized predator on honeybees. It is well known that they never visit flowers but are eager to raid hives whenever possible. I was discussing this with Michael Tweedy some time ago and he put forward the theory that the squeak of the Death's-head may have no particular significance at all, but be merely a secondary consequence of the moth blowing air through the tongue to clear it after feeding on sticky honey.

This suggestion interested me very much and as I happened to have a live female Death's-head at the time, reared from a pupa imported from Hungary, I decided to try an experiment. The moth was then about five days old. It had not been fed at all, but was very lively and squeaked loudly when touched. I bought a comb of capped honey and placed the moth upon it. It crawled all over the comb, but did not at first attempt to feed, possibly disturbed by the bright light which was shining on it for photographic purposes. After some minutes I picked up the moth, pulled the tongue forward and guided it into a cell which I had uncapped. The moth immediately became silent and stopped struggling and probed its tongue up to the hilt into the cell. It showed its appreciation by a slight quivering of the wings and a continuous movement of the head from side to side, as it sucked up the honey.

After a few moments it withdrew its tongue and immediately inserted it in the next cell which had also been uncapped. I wanted to see if it could easily pierce the wax, so when I considered it had almost emptied the second cell I picked it up, without any protest this time, and placed it in the middle of the comb. Without any help from me it at once dug its tongue through the nearest cap and began to feed again greedily. I soon decided that it might become ill if allowed to gorge much longer so I picked it up again, but there was no squeak, only a curious clicking sound, which clearly showed that the squeaking mechanism was either blocked with honey or that the moth was unable to pump any air through the tongue when its stomach was well filled.

The insect was now returned to its cage and every hour or so I touched it, in order to find out when its 'voice' would return. The clicking noise was repeated several times, but it was not until five hours after feeding that it was able to squeak again. This long time lag made me inclined to think that it was the full stomach rather than a blocked tongue which made squeaking impossible. I was unfortunately unable to repeat the experiment, because the following day the moth died. Whether this was due to over-eating, or possibly because it had not received food early enough in life, I could not tell.

There are many records of Death's-head moths seen leaving bee-hives pursued by the bees and apparently unable to fly, whether as a result of having imbibed too much honey, or because they have been stung, it is not easy to ascertain. In one instance a specimen was captured when leaving a hive in this condition and kept for a fortnight before it died, which seems to indicate that the bees could not have done it much harm. A very interesting record from the beginning of this century suggests that most of the moths which enter hives, and are later discovered dead among the combs, meet their fate because they fail to find a way out, rather than because they are stung to death.

A swarm of bees built their combs in a house at Rovigno in Italy between the window pane and a closed blind and their activities could be watched through the glass. During September and October a great many Death's-heads pushed their way into this unusual hive through openings in the blind, fed on the honey, were unable to find their way out again and became prisoners among the bees. The moths invariably arrived after dark, and during the daytime they could be observed and it was clear that the bees worried them a good deal. On 1st October a hundred imprisoned moths, most of them dead, were removed by the director of a nearby zoological station and some time later fifty-four others were collected in the same way. Other stories of Death's-heads in bee-hives make it clear that they do cause a considerable disturbance among the bees and they have even on occasions compelled a colony to desert the hive.

The Aurelians, that 'ingenious and curious body of people' which met regularly at the Swan Tavern in Change Alley in the 1760s, used to talk about this great moth as the 'Bee Tyger'. One of the members, the famous Moses Harris, figured the moth and its caterpillar feeding on jasmine, in his well-known work on natural history entitled *The Aurelian*. The original drawings for this book are now in the care of the Trustees of the Natural History Museum at South Kensington in London.

I cannot remember when I saw my first live Death's-head Hawk-moth, but I do recall helping my father to look for the caterpillars in the back garden of a house at Bexleyheath in Kent, where one had been found earlier in the day. In those days I always travelled about the countryside on the metal step of my father's bicycle and I endured my aching leg with fortitude because I was infected by his enthusiasm for collecting. As soon as we got to the garden it was obvious that there had been more than one caterpillar; the yellowing haulm was stripped of leaves right down to the stalks along half a row.

My father groaned at this sight and felt certain that all the caterpillars had pupated, but nevertheless we began to search. It was quite a long time before my father found one and when he did he called me over, but I could not see it. Then he pointed to a thick yellow object almost hidden on the underside of a leaf; the blue and white diagonal lines along its yellow body so effectively broke up its shape that it was nearly invisible to my untrained eye. Encouraged by this I went on searching and we found two more lurking under the leaves. I cannot remember what happened to them, but presumably the pupae died, as I have no recollection of any moths emerging.

Since then I have found, or been sent, many Death's-head caterpillars and I now know how to treat them. Whenever I get one I put it in a large breeding cage, previously filled to a depth of about six inches with slightly moist, friable soil. I do not put the food plant in water, but throw in fresh potato leaves twice a day until the caterpillar stops feeding and begins to wander. This urge to crawl away from the food plant and find a suitable place for pupation is very strong and if conditions in the cage are not to its liking the caterpillar will sometimes walk around for days. A friend of mine had one patrolling his cage for three days and nights non-stop! Normally the larva will burrow underground within twenty-four hours and I find it helps to put a layer of damp moss on top of the soil.

On no account must the caterpillar be disturbed while it is constructing its underground chamber, but after a fortnight it is usually safe to dig the pupa up. It is essential, in this country, either to force the moth out in a high temperature of 85° to 90°F., when it will emerge within a month, or to keep the pupa warm indoors otherwise it will not survive. In its native surroundings, in Egypt and in the Middle East, it breeds all the year round and has no prolonged resting period in the pupa.

I find that an old glass aquarium tank makes the best incubator for forcing moth pupae and it can easily be heated by an electric light bulb. I put a layer of moist peat at the bottom, lay the pupa on this and cover it with damp moss. I put a sheet of glass over the top of the tank, raising one end slightly for ventilation and the bulb hangs on its cord inside. The ideal temperature is 85°F. Slight fluctuations do not seem to do any harm but it is important to keep the moss just a little damp all the time.

Even when pupae are forced, the duration of this stage varies very much and may be anything from three weeks to eight or nine weeks, although about a month is the usual time. The actual expansion of the wings, after the moth has emerged, takes about forty minutes and in captivity most of the moths seem to break out of their shells between eleven and twelve at night. As soon as it has freed itself from the pupal case, the moth becomes very active, running quickly up the side of the cage, until it finds a suitable place where it can cling, often squeaking in the process.

After the wings have dried the moth can usually be made to squeak quite easily by touching it or irritating it in some way. The squeak is loud and distinct, and while squeaking the moth raises its body and hunches the thorax and sometimes lashes out with its two front legs, indicating that the noise is produced with the aid of movement to force air through an aperture. A great many conflicting theories have been put forward in an effort to explain how the moth produces this sound. It is now generally accepted that it is not caused by friction of any one part of the body against another, but is the result of air being forced through a narrow slit on the upper surface of the base of the tongue, while entering or being expelled from a special air sac or sucking bladder which lies between the tongue and the stomach. The sound may be a means of signalling between the sexes as well as a defensive noise and observers have noticed that if one moth in a cage begins to squeak, others will answer. The fully fed caterpillar is also capable of making a noise, which was described in 1763 by Scopoli in Latin: '*larva irritata stridens*'. This noise is more like a crackle than a squeak and has been compared to the sound made by an electric spark or the noise produced by clicking a finger nail, and it seems to be generally agreed that it is made by the hard chitinous jaws, or mandibles, gnashing together.

Some years ago I was staying with a friend at Chester who, when he took me to his house, told me that he had a pair of Death's-heads which had emerged the previous evening and hoped to obtain a pairing. We decided to sit up together and watch. A muslin-covered cage stood in a corner of the room and the only light we dared show came from the door into the hall which was left ajar. I remember seeing the moths dimly crawling about the walls of the cage, while a great deal of squeaking went on from time to time, but they never took to the wing and I saw no evidence of the female 'calling'. The normal behaviour of a female hawk-moth is to hang from the top of the cage with her scent organs protruding and pulsating, and it is then that the male is attracted and pairing takes place. On this occasion, however, we finally went to bed disappointed, and undoubtedly, as is almost invariably the case with forced hawk-moths, the insects were infertile.

There are no records, as far as I know, of paired Death's-heads being found in the wild, but the late H. W. Head of Scarborough, a noted breeder of Lepidoptera, once observed a pairing of these moths in captivity. The female did not hang up to call in the usual way but flew around, squeaking all the time. The male responded by also taking to the wing and grasped the female in flight. The pair then settled, but the male did not turn round to face the opposite way as hawk-moths invariably do, but clung close to the female's body, grasping her with his legs. Unfortunately no eggs were obtained.

On the occasions when Death's-head moth caterpillars have been found in large numbers in Britain, they have been picked up in potato fields near the sea, indicating that the migrating moths have laid their eggs on the first suitable plants they have come across. Entomologists have also noticed that the majority of the larvae are near the edge of the field, rather than in the middle. When first hatching they are a pale yellowish-green, but quickly darken when they begin to feed. In the early stages the horn is long and dark and the caterpillar is a rather light, frosted green, rough to the touch and with faint white stripes. After the third skin change the colours become more vivid and the stripes assume their blue or purple tint, while the horn turns yellow. After the fourth change the horn shrinks and thickens and bends downwards.

While feeding, the larvae always sit on the undersides of the leaves where they are very well camouflaged, and while resting during the day they take up the typical sphinx position, just like the Privet Hawk caterpillar. In Africa and the Middle East they feed up very quickly, completing their growth in fifteen days, and the adult moth often emerges only nineteen days after pupation; but in Britain, under cooler conditions, the metamorphosis takes considerably longer.

Some years ago Mr L. G. Hulls made a very careful study of a number of Death's-head caterpillars which he found during 1938 and 1939 and recorded his findings in *The Entomologist*. He particularly investigated the loss in weight which occurs before pupation. He found that the loss begins, as it does in the Privet Hawk, a couple of days before feeding stops and then continues rapidly for three days, gradually slowing down until pupation takes place. A good deal of this loss is caused by the caterpillar voiding a quantity of a clear, colourless liquid, both from the mouth and the anus. On testing, this liquid proved to be highly alkaline and he noticed that the caterpillars apparently deliberately crawled through it and coated themselves with the fluid, which gave them an oily, semi-transparent appearance.

During this period they also become much darker, taking on a brownish tint, and a bright blue band appears along the centre of the back. A decided restlessness sets in and the larvae begin to wander, walking quickly and deliberately, searching for a suitable pupation site and pushing their way with great strength into holes and crevices. Mr Hulls found that a caterpillar could raise a lid which was held down with a $\frac{3}{4}$-pound weight. After the restless period begins the larva makes a loud clicking noise when handled and this ability continues while it shrinks and becomes short and springy and apt to bend violently backwards and forwards if touched. In nature the larva would most probably have dug itself down into the soil by this time and the strong wriggling movements, combined with the fluid which is voided, help to consolidate the walls of the pupal cell.

When the pupa first emerges from the larval skin it is cream-coloured with a slight greenish tinge on the upper side of the abdomen, but within thirty hours it darkens to a mahogany brown all over. The newly formed pupa is very sensitive to light, which it obviously dislikes, and it immediately begins to wriggle and even turns right over if a bright light is focused upon it.

In Europe larvae of the Death's-head have been found from June to the end of November and even in December. Generally they are more plentiful in the autumn than earlier in the summer, but north of the Alps late caterpillars are often killed by spells of cold wet weather and practically all the pupae appear to die during the winter, although a few reports of moths taken very early in the year suggest that they may on rare occasions be able to survive. On 27th March 1943 a Death's-head Hawk-moth was found on the wall of a farmhouse at Stradbally near Waterford in Ireland and it was in such perfect condition that the man who found it came to the conclusion that it could only just have emerged.

In Africa the moth has two or three generations in the year, possibly even more, and the larvae can be found in Morocco and Algiers throughout the winter and the same applies to South Africa. The moths which arrive in Britain in the autumn are probably the progeny of a previous generation bred in Europe, from early immigrants from the south.

Although Death's-head larvae are nearly always found on potato plants in Britain, they will feed on a wide variety of foods, including most of the poisonous plants belonging to the potato family, such as deadly nightshade (*Atropa belladonna*), woody nightshade (*Solanum dulcamara*), the black nightshade (*Solanum nigrum*) and the thorn apple (*Datura stramonium*). In eastern Europe they often feed on the so-called tea plant (*Lycium barbarum*) and they have also been found on tobacco plants such as *Nicotiana rustica* and *Nicotiana tabacum* as well as on jasmine, olive and honeysuckle. In the south the larvae are often parasitized, especially by Tachinid flies, which in general appearance very much resemble the house-fly, except that they are larger in size; but in Germany and in Great Britain very few parasitized caterpillars have been found.

Nowadays the Death's-head is a rare moth in the British Isles—very rare might be a better description. The practice of spraying the potato fields to prevent disease has virtually ruled out the possibility of another great '*atropos* year'. But there was a time, actually in the summer of 1846, when the caterpillars were so common in Thanet, in the Margate area, that farmers collected them to feed to their poultry. Scanning the scientific journals of those days I came upon another record from Kent where a Mr Russell reported that over a hundred larvae were found at Ashford twelve years later, while in 1905 the well-known author Charles G. Barrett recorded in *The Entomologist* that one collector bought and sold over a thousand pupae dug up in Thanet. In the same year A. M. Morley, the Folkestone entomologist, whom I have known since I was a boy, remembers talking to a Mr A. G. Peyton who told him that he had found about three hundred caterpillars at Ramsgate. There is also a record of a potato field in Norfolk being completely stripped of leaves until nothing but the bare stalks remained.

If you study the entomological magazines of the last twenty-five years you will notice that except for 1956, when 381 moths were individually recorded, the annual average is a mere 14 insects. The previous record in 1933 was 101 moths. The actual number of those seen in 1956 naturally cannot give a true picture of the magnitude of the migration, for many thousands of Death's-heads must have escaped notice. Had they arrived in early summer and laid their eggs we might have experienced a repetition of the plague of caterpillars just over a century ago.

The first Death's-head in 1956 was caught on 11th June but the main migration took place in September. One thing that emerges very clearly from the records is that the Death's-heads did not come from France but further over from the east via the Low Countries. Other evidence suggests that their route may have been through Italy and Germany as well. During September alone 243 moths were recorded in Holland by Mr B. J. Lempke, who runs an organization similar to our Insect Immigration Committee which has its headquarters at Rothamsted Experimental Station at Harpenden, Herts.

After a B.B.C. broadcast on the Death's-head invasion I received many letters from people who had seen the moths and one of these was certainly unique. It was written by a yachtsman who had been at sea in the Channel on the night of 12th September, about fifteen miles north of Dunkirk. The night was calm and foggy and as dawn broke he noticed that the rigging looked blurred and thick. On looking closer he found a great number of Death's-heads clinging to the ropes where they had obviously pitched during the night. Unfortunately he did not notice in which direction they flew off during the early morning as his attention was too occupied with the difficulty of navigating in the fog.

Other letters described how moths were found sitting on breakwaters, hiding in the porches of sea-side houses and in sheds and gardens. One moth had crawled under a coat thrown across the bonnet of a car and when the owner came to put it on the Death's-head flew out and hit him in the face. Near Newcastle a very lively moth was captured flying among the lights of a merry-go-round at a local flower show. The ladies who came to decorate the church at Fangfoss in York for the harvest festival in October found a dead moth in one of the pews. And finally the experience of a child, Rose Voelcker, aged nine, who told in her own words: 'I was on holiday in Cornwall, Langford Hill near Bude, in the second week of September, one mild evening when I was reading in bed before Mummy came up to shut me down. A Death's-head Hawk-moth came in through the window and settled on the wall. Then I suddenly thought I had a mouse in the room because it was making such a noise when it was walking about on the ceiling, and I did hear it squeak.'

The Convolvulus Hawk

HERSE CONVOLVULI

Haunts. The Convolvulus Hawk ranges over a very wide area and is found in Europe, Asia, Africa, Australia and Polynesia. In Europe it is a migrant rather than a true resident moth, sometimes very plentiful, at other times rare. In years when large numbers of these moths migrate northwards it reaches the Orkneys, Scandinavia and Finland and it has been found in almost every part of the British Isles, including the Scilly Isles and Ireland. It is, however, most frequently found in the southern and south-eastern counties which lie closest to the Continent. The moths travel up through Europe from Africa and the near East, crossing the Alps and gradually make their way northward. In Britain they are seldom seen until July or August, or even later, but occasional specimens have been found in June and there is even a record of one caught at Folkestone on 20th May 1948. Although the Convolvulus Hawk does lay its eggs on these migratory journeys and the larvae develop and pupate, the moths of the next generation fail to survive as they either emerge in the autumn when the weather is already turning cold, or succumb in the pupal stage during the winter. In its native countries the moth is continuously brooded, with three or even four generations in the year.

The Egg. Although the Convolvulus Hawk is a large moth it lays an exceptionally small egg, less than half the size of the Privet Hawk egg and bright blue-green in colour when first laid. Later it changes to a more yellowish-green, and when near to hatching the upper surface becomes depressed. A single female can lay over 250 eggs, but among those moths which emerge in Europe during the late summer or autumn many appear to be infertile, and even if some of them do lay eggs, few of these hatch. In nature the eggs are laid on the leaves of bindweed, both on the field bindweed (*Convolvulus arvensis*) and on the hedge bindweed (*Convolvulus sepium*) and also sometimes on cultivated species of the same genus, such as the morning glory (*Ipomea coerulea*) and others. The eggs hatch in fourteen to seventeen days.

The Caterpillar. The larvae of this big moth are extremely variable, and even those which are the progeny of a single female may differ entirely in appearance. The French entomologist Boisduval divided them into two main categories, green and brown, and each of these into three subdivisions, and there are innumerable variations between them so that, in fact, hardly any two larvae are exactly alike. They even vary in size and to some extent in behaviour.

A fully fed Convolvulus Hawk caterpillar measures a good 10 or 11 cm in length and carries a curved glossy horn at the end of its body. It is of fairly uniform thickness but the first five segments taper gently towards the head, which is rather small. Each segment is subdivided into eight sections, giving the larva a corrugated appearance, but the skin, which is very wrinkled immediately after a moult, becomes quite smooth to the touch when the larva has been feeding for some days.

In the dark form the general ground colour is a deep sepia, mottled with brown or ochreous yellow. Along the sides are somewhat indistinct oblique stripes with a pale spot at the top and below the spiracles runs an almost white, irregular line. Along the back are two lines of paler brown, broken by darker transverse lines. The spiracles are black, the head striped in black and brown. The green form is a rich, dark green, heavily patterned with black oblique marks which are joined to form a line at the top, leaving the centre of the back green. The first four segments bear a double row of black spots which later join to form continuous streaks. The spiracles are black and the head is striped with black. Between these two extreme forms are, as already mentioned, a great many intermediate types, including a green form with almost white diagonal stripes and another which lacks these markings completely but is patterned instead with longitudinal rows of dark spots.

The Pupa. The larva burrows down into the earth before pupating and hollows out a chamber by wriggling and rolling, consolidating the sides so that they become firm, in very much the same way as the Death's-head behaves. The pupa is unmistakable, being large, glossy and rich mahogany in colour with a finely corrugated tongue case which is curved like a jug handle, joining again with the rest of the body some distance from the tip, which is bent up towards the head. The large eyes are clearly visible and so are the antennae. The wingcases are long and the pupa rather resembles in general shape that of the Privet Hawk, although it is bigger and heavier, measuring over 5 cm in length. It is mobile and lively and will twitch strongly when touched.

The Adult Moth. The Convolvulus Hawk is not a colourful moth and apart from the bands of pale pink, black and white which decorate the abdomen, the main colouring is grey and brown, without any distinct or remarkable pattern. The moth is obviously built for rapid and sustained flight, with its long narrow wings and its smooth, tapering streamlined body. The fore-wings are finely mottled and pencilled in grey and brown, with a concentration of brown colouring near the centre, especially in the male. In this brown area are two distinct short black streaks and there is a third, more jagged line near the tip of the wing. The hind-wings are grey, banded with brown, and the fringes of the wings are coloured in alternate white and grey-brown elongated spots. The head is pale grey, the thorax a darker shade of grey. The most remarkable feature of the Convolvulus Hawk is its tremendously long tongue, which exceeds the total length of the body and in a large specimen will measure nearly 13 cm in length. When not in use, the tongue is rolled up like a watch spring between the prominent grey palpi on the underside of the head. The antennae are greyish-white and considerably larger in the male than in the female. The male also has on the underside of the body two tufts of scent scales which give off a distinct smell of musk.

The great attraction of this large and interesting moth lies in its irregular appearance and its remarkable flying skill, which many people have been fortunate enough to get a chance to admire when the moth has visited their gardens at early dusk, while it is still light enough to discern its shadowy form hovering before the flowers. It moves with incredible speed from one plant to the next and then suddenly vanishes, so quickly that the eye cannot follow its flight. The moth is easily scared and any sudden noise or movement will send it away, but a quiet observer, moving deliberately and carefully, can often get really close enough to watch the moth probing its long tongue into tubular flowers. It is especially fond of sweet tobacco flowers, which exhale a strong perfume in the evening and it will also visit petunias and lilies.

Barrett, in his *British Lepidoptera,* says: 'If no sudden movement is made to alarm it, the creature seems by no means timid and even at times familiar and inquisitive. I have repeatedly seen it when nearly approached hover up and seem to look in my face, so that its gleaming lustrous eyes were distinctly visible looking into my own, then flash past my shoulder, and return to the flowers. It has even been seen to approach and inspect a brilliant scarlet striped jacket on one of the lads and apparently touch the bright colour with its tongue as though desirous of ascertaining what new kind of brilliant flower had entered the garden.'

A contributor to *The Entomologist's Record* in 1962, described how he had observed the moths in Italy coming to feed from the flowers in a garden punctually at 7.20 each evening and disappearing again at 7.45, but there are also records of the moths being seen much later, especially on moonlight nights. There are also quite a number of records of Convolvulus Hawks on the wing during the day. Rough weather does not seem to deter them and many observers have noticed that they appear more fearless than usual on windy, wet nights.

The rapidly vibrating wings of the Convolvulus Hawk-moth produce a distinct humming sound which can easily be heard on a still night, and very often its presence is realized only by this sound and the sight of nodding flower heads, because the grey moth itself is almost invisible in the dusk. It will sometimes come flying in through open windows and is certainly attracted by light. During the day moths have been discovered in all kinds of different places, settled on walls and fences, on the ground, inside a motor car, on clothes hung out to dry, on gate-posts or on almost any other firm object where they can cling and fold their grey wings like a roof over the body. Resting like this they are very difficult to detect, and resemble, as much as anything, a piece of grey well-weathered wood. On one occasion, when a female was found in a conservatory in Cornwall, it was covered with a bell cloche to prevent it escaping and the next morning a male was found sitting beside the cloche, evidently attracted to the captive female, whose scent must have filtered out under the edge of the cloche.

The Convolvulus Hawk is usually found in Britain every year, but it does not appear in large numbers more than every ten or fifteen years, and these huge migrations, which are as yet unexplained, seem to coincide with migrations of Death's-heads. Going back in time it appears that the year 1846, which was a notable one for Death's-heads, was also an exceptional year for Convolvulus Hawks and that season the big grey moths were found everywhere, even in the Orkneys and Shetlands. When they first arrived they came in such massed formation that one man swept up five of them at once in his net, in a garden near Canterbury. In 1875 sixty Convolvulus Hawk-moths were captured in one garden at Birchington on the Kent coast and there are several other similar records from the south and east coastal areas. As the moths spread out on their flight northwards they appeared less abundant. The year 1945, which was an exceptional one for migrations of both butter-flies and moths, also brought a number of Convolvulus Hawks to Britain.

At the beginning of this century, in 1901, as many as a hundred larvae were found. This is unusual, because although there are numerous records of moths being seen and caught, comparatively few caterpillars have been discovered, and this has led entomologists to believe that the moth does not find our climate very suitable for breeding. The majority of the larvae found here have been discovered in potato fields, feeding on the lesser bindweed, and the moths seem to favour this type of locality for egg laying. Quite a number of pupae have also been un-earthed during potato digging. I was once called to inspect a clump of bindweed in a garden in Devon, where the leaves had been eaten away, and the large droppings or 'frass', on the ground indicated that a big caterpillar had been feeding, but I was too late and the Convolvulus Hawk had departed on its first and last walk.

The general experience among people who have tried to breed these moths in captivity in Britain has been that only a very small percentage of the eggs ever hatch. A large number are completely infertile, others begin to form up but fail to hatch, and among the larvae which do hatch many die before becoming full-fed. The reason for this very low fertility is not clear, but it is probably due to lack of warmth, or possibly a shortage of suitable food.

When hatching, the young caterpillar eats a hole in the side of the shell, but does not go on eating it after crawling out. It is $3\frac{1}{2}$ mm long and light yellow in colour with a slightly darker head, and is very thin and delicate looking. The anal horn is nearly straight, half as long as the body, and also quite pale in colour, but soon becomes black. A few hours after hatching the caterpillar begins to feed, sitting on the under-side of a leaf and nibbling a hole right through it. In the early stages the young larvae seem to prefer to feed at night, resting along the mid-rib of the leaf during the day. Their appetites are small at this stage and they grow rather slowly, gradually changing from yellow to light green.

After the first moult the skin remains green but other markings on the body begin to appear, varying a great deal between individuals. Detailed descriptions of the growth and appearance of larvae reared in captivity show that they vary, not only in appearance, but also in the time they take between one skin change and the next, and the size they reach before this takes place. One of the larvae described cast its first skin when ten days old and 9 mm in length, while another moulted for the first time at the age of twelve days, when it was still only 6 mm long. Most of the old skins were devoured before the caterpillars started to feed again on the leaves, now eating more voraciously from the edge of the leaf inwards, and feeding, with intervals for rest, both during the day and at night.

The Convolvulus Hawk caterpillars make no special attempt at concealing themselves, but remain all the time clinging to the bindweed stems, moving only just enough to reach the next leaf when the nearest one has been consumed. The belief held by the early entomologists that these caterpillars burrowed into the soil during the day has been disproved and if they are placed on the ground they return at once to the food plant.

A very interesting thing about the two independent rearing experiments chronicled in detail by Derek Ashwell and C. M. R. Pitman in 1945 and 1959 is that in the first case the solitary larva, which was of the dark brown type changed its skin four times before pupating, while in the other instance the two larvae, one brown and one green, underwent only three changes. The first larva went underground on the fifty-seventh day after hatching, having wandered for less than twelve hours. Of the other two, the green caterpillar burrowed rather quickly into the earth thirty-seven days after hatching, while the brown one, which never grew as large as the green larva, wandered about for several days before going to earth on the fortieth day. This particular larva made its earthen cell against the transparent perspex side of the cage so that it could be plainly seen and it did not change into a pupa until it had been in the cocoon for seventeen days. Observations on the speed of the larvae, during their very restless period between ceasing to feed and burrowing into the earth, showed that they moved a distance of about one yard per minute, and at this rate, a prolonged period of wandering would take a larva several hundred yards from its original feeding place.

It is always very difficult to investigate what actually happens within the underground cell when the larval skin is cast to reveal the pupa, but a series of remarkable colour photographs taken fairly recently by a German entomologist, Herr Werner Zepf, show this process in great detail. When the pupa first appears, gradually wriggling itself free of the larval skin, it is clear green in colour and the tongue case is quite short. Before the pupal shell hardens and turns first buff and then mahogany brown, the tongue case grows, bends under at the tip and then touches the body and adheres to form the characteristic 'jug handle' which, once the skin has hardened, is not nearly as fragile as it looks.

The time spent in the pupal stage varies a good deal. In its native haunts the moth normally only spends two or three weeks as a pupa but odd individuals may remain inert much longer, sometimes for several months. People who have bred the larvae in captivity in Britain usually attempt to force the moths by keeping them very warm indoors, and by this method the metamorphosis is completed in anything from three weeks to three months. Here again individuals vary greatly. A note in *The Entomologist* for June 1947 records six larvae which pupated between 16th and 23rd November 1945. One of these, a male, emerged on 17th February 1946 after the pupae had been kept in a fairly steady temperature of 70°F., while the remainder were all alive, but still in the pupal stage at the time of writing the note in June 1946. Another record from 1937 tells of four larvae, collected almost fully fed in the wild in the middle of September, which, after forcing began on 25th September, all emerged within a month, the first one on 14th October. Three of these were females, one a male, and they all appeared at the same time of day, between eight and nine in the evening.

The Oleander Hawk

DAPHNIS NERII

Haunts. This large and very beautiful moth is a native of Africa and the southern parts of Asia. It breeds also in southern Europe during the summer. It is fairly common in the Middle East and apparently survives the winter there. North of the Alps it is only a migrant and in Britain merely an occasional vagrant. Although it has been found as far north as Aberdeen and has also appeared in Norway, Sweden and on the borders between Russia and Finland, the moths only reach such northern latitudes in very small numbers and there has never been a really large migration of Oleander Hawks in Britain. Those moths which have been taken in the British Isles have been widely distributed and a surprisingly large number have been found in towns, settled on pavements or on houses, probably attracted by bright lights during the night.

The Egg. The eggs are rather small for such a large moth, and resemble very closely those of the Privet Hawk, being light green in colour and almost round. They are laid singly, but often quite close together, both on the upper and the under surface of the leaves, as well as on the leaf stalks of oleander bushes (*Nerium oleander*) and also sometimes on periwinkle (*Vinca minor* or *Vinca major*).

The Caterpillar. The fully fed caterpillar is very large, measuring 12 to 15 cm in length, and it has a rather short, bent and very rough horn, which is yellow with a black tip. The ground colour of the body is normally a rather pale blue-green, shading to a yellowish-green on the front segments and the head. Rather high up on the body on either side runs a broad white streak with a blue shading below it, starting from the fifth segment and extending to the horn. Along and above this line there is usually a sprinkling of white spots, bordered with green or greenish-blue. On the fourth segment, on either side of the body, is a large black-ringed spot which is pale blue in the centre, shading to indigo blue at the edge, and quite often it appears to be made up of

66

two separate halves. The underside of the body is a pale grey-green and the legs are pinkish. The spiracles are quite small and black, ringed with white. Before pupating the caterpillar assumes a livid orange-pink ground colour with the back, from the fifth segment to the tail, a dark blue-black. The eye-spot also turns black, while the spots along the sides remain white.

The Pupa.   The caterpillar spins a large cocoon of strong brown silk on the ground before pupating, entwining leaves and rubbish with the strands, and turns into a pupa about five days later. The pupa is large, measuring $7\frac{1}{2}$ cm in length, but it is not as thick as that of the Death's-head Hawk-moth. The colour is a light brown or terracotta, sprinkled with tiny black dots, particularly on the wingcases. The spiracles are very clearly marked with quite large round black spots. A black line runs down the body between the wingcases, continues as a broken line over the head and then more clearly down the thorax along the back, but fades away on the abdominal segments. The sharp point at the tip of the body is unusually short and quite straight. The adult moths often emerge only fifteen days after pupation but the metamorphosis may take considerably longer, even up to six weeks. It is unlikely that the pupae ever overwinter in Europe except possibly in Spain or Sicily and even in the south of France the winter weather is not warm enough for them to emerge successfully.

The Adult Moth.   The Oleander Hawk-moth measures between 9 and 11 cm across the wings with a body length of about $5\frac{1}{2}$ cm. The front margin of the fore-wings curves gently towards the tip, giving a stream-lined appearance, and the wings are most beautifully marbled and marked. The ground colour is a rich sage green with gracefully curved patterns of pale green and cream. Near the front edge of each fore-wing, close to the body, is a round green spot surrounded by a ring of cream, giving the impression of an eye on either side of the thorax. Along the inner margin, starting near the body, runs a pink band, which then bends upwards towards the front margin but fades into cream before reaching it. The greater part of the hind-wings, from the base outwards, is a dark pinkish-grey edged with a creamy-white line, followed by a band of dull green fringed with white. The area near the anal angle is creamy white. The head and thorax are the same green colour as the fore-wings, marked with pinkish-grey lines. The abdomen is green in the centre and ochreous yellow at the sides and the divisions between the segments are marked by thin white lines. The legs and antennae are a pale creamy yellow.

The Oleander Hawk

It is a pity that this splendid moth is so seldom seen in the northern parts of Europe. It is a powerful flyer and well able to reach the shores of Britain, but as oleander is rare and periwinkle not very common either, migrations to the north would in any case be fruitless. The moth is definitely a tropical and subtropical insect and does not have the same strong urge to migrate as the Striped Hawk and the Hummingbird Hawk-moth. A large proportion of the Oleander Hawks found in this country have been picked up in urban areas. This may possibly just be a coincidence because they are more likely to be seen in such places than among green leaves in the countryside, or it may be due to the attraction of bright city lights at night.

The first Oleander Hawk recorded in Britain flew into a drawing room in Dover in 1833 and another was found near the pier the following year, obviously both visitors from across the Channel who had settled in the first convenient spot. Since then there have been records from Birmingham and Sheffield, Glasgow, Hartlepool and Poplar. One was found on London Bridge and another picked up in the gutter in Queen Victoria Street while a third was found in Bishopsgate Street. In 1950 an Oleander Hawk was found in Bristol and in 1948 a schoolboy discovered one in the school yard at Bagilt in Flintshire. In October 1946 one was found sitting on a pavement in Ealing and on 30th June 1950 a businessman on his way to London noticed one on the station platform at Greenford in Middlesex. It was in perfect condition and when he picked it up to put it out of harm's way it took wing and flew down into the gardens below the station. On 1st October 1948 a lady living at Leigh-on-Sea discovered an Oleander Hawk clinging to the bonnet of her car. It was an unusually large and fine specimen but unfortunately it battered itself badly inside a box before it was handed over to an entomologist next day.

Apart from a very old record dating from 1859, when two larvae were said to have been found feeding on periwinkle in a potato field near Eastbourne, there is, as far as I know, only one instance recorded of larvae having been discovered wild in Britain. This was during the last war when somebody wandering round the deserted garden of a bombed house in the Midlands found two caterpillars feeding on an oleander bush growing in the ruins of a shattered greenhouse. This may well be the only time a migrant Oleander Hawk has ever been able to find its proper food plant in Britain, because the few oleanders grown here are nearly always well protected under glass.

In public gardens on the Continent, both in France, Switzerland and Germany, oleanders in large pots are often stood outside in the parks during the summer and there are a number of records of caterpillars being found even as far north as Hamburg and Berlin. Further south, where the climate is warm enough for oleanders to grow out of doors, the larvae sometimes become a pest and gardeners in Italy and even in the south of France are often obliged to pick them off the bushes where they devour both the flowers and the leaves.

The young larvae are usually found on the side shoots low down on the bushes, feeding on the tender tips, but larger larvae seem to prefer the branches nearer the top. Invariably however they like the young leaves best and also greedily eat the flowers. Smaller leaves are eaten completely, including the stalks, but in the case of slightly older and tougher leaves, the caterpillars often nibble a portion out of each side and leave the rest. When all the young leaves on one shoot have been consumed the larva crawls back to the main stem and then makes its way up to the next side shoot, to start feeding again at the tip.

When resting between meals, the Oleander Hawk normally remains stretched out on the twigs, but with the thorax contracted and the head slightly raised. If it is touched or the twig is shaken, the caterpillar suddenly arches its back by bending the head down under the body until it almost touches the first pair of pro-legs. This movement stretches the skin on the thorax and enlarges the blue eye-spot, which immediately becomes very startling in appearance. This habit is undoubtedly a defensive one, aimed at frightening away an enemy.

When the larvae are fully fed and have stopped eating, they smear their bodies all over with fluid secreted from their mouths, and during this process the skin becomes dull and dark and the eye-spot turns almost completely black. The following day, as soon as it grows warm in the morning, the caterpillars become restless, crawl down from the bushes and begin to wander, their dark colouring giving them a protective resemblance to the earth. Entomologists who have bred Oleander Hawks in captivity have noticed that the moths generally emerge in the evening, between eight and eleven, and take a couple of hours to dry their wings. They do not fly at all until dawn the following morning. Unlike the Convolvulus and the Striped Hawk, the Oleander Hawk is not very often seen at flowers and possibly it flies later in the night when it is less likely to be observed.

When Oleander Hawks do come to Britain, they usually arrive here in late summer or early autumn and these moths are members of the second generation, bred in the south. Some have been found in Britain as late as October and even November. The British specimens have, most likely, come from southern Europe, and are the progeny of an early summer migration from Africa. In its native environment in Africa and India, the moth has several generations a year. In the south of France larvae of the first brood are found during July and the second-brood caterpillars are fully fed by the end of September.

The larvae occur in different colour forms and are occasionally of a pale ochreous ground colour, with a purple ring round the eye-spot instead of the usual indigo blue. This form is rare in nature, but Mr D. G. Sevastopulo, experimenting in India with a number of larvae, came to the conclusion that over-crowding was the cause of this unusual colour form. Although he had reared hundreds of the Oleander Hawk larvae he only ever had six of the pale type, two of these in a batch of thirty-five accidentally very crowded caterpillars, and four more in a lot of twenty larvae which were deliberately kept in close proximity to each other in small glass jars.

Bronze-coloured larvae have also been found, with the front segments rosy red. The newly hatched caterpillar is pale yellow with an unusually long black horn. After the first moult it turns green and the horn gradually becomes less prominent during succeeding skin changes. It is said that larvae which are fed exclusively on oleander flowers and kept very warm produce bigger and finer moths than those which feed on the leaves. The moths do not vary very much, except in size, but sometimes odd specimens have been found with the sage green colour replaced by olive-brown and there is also a certain amount of variation in the depth and extent of the pink area on the fore-wing.

The Spurge Hawk

CELERIO EUPHORBIAE

Haunts. On the continent of Europe this attractive moth is widespread and comparatively common in many regions, both inland and by the coast, but it is very seldom found in Great Britain. Records of its capture are not always reliable, because the moth is often confused with the Bedstraw Hawk, which it closely resembles. In those instances when larvae have been found in this country they have usually, although not always, been picked up near the sea, but there are a few records from inland districts in Kent, and other southern counties.

The Egg. The Spurge Hawk lays an almost round, bright green, glossy egg, which is fixed to the food plant. The eggs are deposited either singly or in clusters near the tips of the shoots. The favourite food plant seems to be the sea spurge (*Euphorbia paralias*) or the cypress spurge (*E. cyparissias*). Although the larvae will also eat other varieties of herbaceous spurges, including the common garden weed—the petty spurge—they apparently do not thrive very well on these, at least not in captivity, and seldom complete their development. The eggs hatch from ten to fourteen days after being laid.

The Caterpillar. The Spurge Hawk larva is perhaps the most colourful and richly patterned of any of the hawk-moths. Although it is very variable in colouring, the markings are fairly constant and the caterpillar can therefore easily be identified. When fully grown the larvae measure between 7 and 8 cm in length and are plump and cylindrical, tapering slightly towards the head, which is rounded and rather small. Usually the caterpillars are marked with a bright red streak along the back, joining the red head to the rough red tail horn, which is tipped with black. In some individuals the streak is green instead of red. The feet and the hind-claspers are the same colour and there is often also a red line below the spiracles. A double row of prominent spots runs along either side of the body, set in black transverse bands. These may be

71

yellow, orange, cream, white or even light green in colour. In some larvae there is an additional broken line of red, orange or yellow along each side, between the spots, but often this is missing. The ground colour varies from greenish to grey, olive or bronze-yellow and close examination reveals that this effect is the result of innumerable minute dots of dark and light colouring, running transversely across the body and giving the same effect as a piece of material in which warp and woof are of different colours.

The Pupa. The fully fed caterpillar does not burrow deep into the ground but constructs a silken cocoon only half an inch or so below the surface, weaving leaves and grains of sand into the structure and fixing it firmly into position. The pupa is rather light brown in colour, with the wingcases and segments striped with a darker shade. The spiracles are dark and so is the flattened anal spike. It measures about $4\frac{1}{2}$ cm in length and is compact and cylindrical in shape, tapering gently towards the tail end. The period in the pupa varies tremendously, from just over a fortnight to more than a year.

The Adult Moth. The Spurge Hawk is a rather stocky, compactly built moth with a thick, sharply tapering body and comparatively short wings. The white antennae thicken towards the tip and the head is prominent. The moth measures about $7\frac{1}{2}$ cm in wing-span and just over 3 cm in length of body. The ground colour of the fore-wings is a dull cream, often with a rosy flush in freshly emerged specimens, and there is a general sprinkling of darker scales. A narrow olive-brown band starts at the tip of the wing and widens as it extends to the lower edge. The area between this band and the outer margin of the wing is a light brown colour, and at the base of the wing, close to the body, there is a brownish patch. An irregular blotch of the same colour is situated half-way along the wing, just beneath the front edge, with another, smaller and less distinct spot nearer the tip. The hind-wings are black at the base and have an irregular, jagged black band near the edge. The margin is pale pink and the area inside the band is a bright crimson with a white spot at the inner margin. The head and the thorax are olive-brown with a white streak along either side. The abdomen is the same general colour as the thorax with two black and white streaks on each side, followed by two more white streaks near the tail end.

The Spurge Hawk can hardly be called a regular migrant, but there are a number of genuine records of its appearance in Britain and almost every year one or two are reported. It does occur in the Channel Islands and it is possible that specimens might come from there or from Brittany on board ships to the southern Channel ports and records from Dover, Folkestone, Deal and Southampton seem to suggest that in some instances at least this may be the case. A female moth, flying ashore from a ship in the evening and laying her eggs wherever the food plant can be found, would also produce enough larvae for at least a few to be discovered, and records for larvae are more numerous than for adult moths.

Only on one occasion were they found in any numbers, however, and that was early in the nineteenth century at Braunton Burrows in Devon, where a certain Mr W. Raddon, a dealer in Lepidoptera, claimed

The graceful and elegant Spurge Hawk is seen
here clinging to the flower head of a spurge plant
whose leaves provide food for the caterpillars.

×2

that he found large numbers of larvae on the sea spurge in the years between 1806 and 1814. Grave doubt has been expressed about the validity of this record, as Raddon was known to import insects from the Continent, but it is impossible to prove whether he was telling the truth or lying. He certainly gave a very vivid description of gathering sea spurge at dusk to feed larvae which he had already collected earlier, and finding, when he returned to the house, that there were already numerous, newly hatched larvae on the plants. I have been to Braunton Burrows, that extensive stretch of sand dunes on the coast, and seen the sea spurge growing there in quantity. It is certainly just the kind of place where one might expect Spurge Hawks to thrive and it is not impossible that migrating moths could have landed there, either from a passing ship or having arrived from the Continent under their own wing power. I know from personal experience that they do lay their eggs in large clusters, so the story of finding numerous newly hatched larvae on the plants gathered after dusk may not be as far-fetched as it sounds.

In September 1889, a young collector is said to have found thirteen larvae on the sea shore in north Cornwall, but most of the other records are only of single caterpillars, or occasionally of two found close together, like those picked up in the Warren at Folkestone in 1937 by a summer visitor from Birmingham. He noticed the caterpillars because his dog stopped and barked at them, obviously startled by their strange appearance. In 1952 a full-grown larva was found on the tow-path beside a marsh at Martham in Norfolk and pupated successfully. The moth, which was a female, did not emerge until 1954.

Adult moths, as already mentioned, are sometimes confused with the Bedstraw Hawk-moth, but there can hardly be any doubt about the specimen taken by the celebrated Charles G. Barrett, author of Barrett's *Lepidoptera*, in his garden at King's Lynn, Norfolk. He tells how: 'It was flying very quietly and gently, at early dusk, about a large bed of verbena, leisurely sipping as it hovered at blossom after blossom, and was captured with the greatest of ease.' There are several other reliable records from different places, including a number of more recent date. In 1902 A. B. Farn discovered to his great surprise a freshly emerged Spurge Hawk clinging to the door knob of his house at Greenhythe, and in 1944 a specimen in good condition was found resting on a tree trunk not far from Farnborough in Hampshire.

In southern Europe—Spain, Italy, Greece and the south of France—the moth is common, and its range extends to Asia Minor. It is especially abundant in warm mountain valleys, both in Switzerland and in the

×2

×1

The Narrow-bordered
Bee Hawk
Hemaris tityus

*A quick and active insect
which flies in the sunshine
and is seen here with
protruding tongue feeding
from a flower. Below, the
moth is seen at rest and the
transparent wings are clearly
visible. The caterpillar feeds
on the leaves of wild
scabious plants and is
difficult to find.*

1

$\times \frac{1}{2}$ $\times \frac{1}{2}$ $\times 1\frac{3}{4}$

The Death's-head Hawk-moth
Acherontia atropos

*The normal resting position of this strange moth is
with its wings folded over the body, but in order to show
the yellow hind-wings this specimen was deliberately
disturbed and is about to take off. Intensive spraying of
potato crops has made the Death's-head increasingly
rare in Europe. The moth has become famous because
of the characteristic skull mark and its ability to squeak.
There are several different colour forms of the caterpillar.*

$\times \frac{3}{4}$

The Convolvulus Hawk-moth
Herse convolvuli

The Convolvulus is noted for its
prodigiously long tongue. Built
for rapid and sustained flight,
it is a great migrant. The
caterpillars have several colour
forms and feed on various
species of bindweed. The curious
pupa has its tongue encased
in a curved sheath.

$\times 1$ $\times \frac{3}{4}$
Pupa   Larva

×1

×¾

The Oleander Hawk-moth
Daphnis nerii

*This large hawk-moth is a native of
Africa and the southern parts of Asia,
and those seen in Europe and Great
Britain have migrated north from their
usual haunts. The two moths illustrated
are a pair and it is indeed unusual to find
two together in Europe. The caterpillars
feed on the leaves of oleander bushes
and a few are discovered most years in
southern Europe, but very seldom north
of the Alps.*

×1¾

×1¾

The Spurge Hawk-moth
Celerio euphorbiae

*This rare visitor to England
does not normally settle with wings
spread, but the moth in the
picture has been disturbed in order
to make it display the hind-wings.
In this position it rocks its body
to and fro in a threatening
manner. The Spurge Hawk is
common on the continent of
Europe and the boldly patterned
caterpillars feed on plants of the
spurge family.*

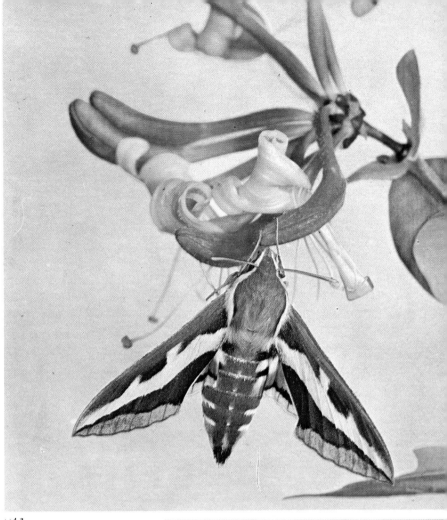

×1¾

The Bedstraw
Hawk-moth
Celerio galii

Another of the migrant
species, which only
rarely comes as far
north as Great Britain.
The moths show a
preference for sandhills
near the coast, where
they lay their eggs on
bedstraw plants. The
rather conspicuous
caterpillars like to sun
themselves on the hot
sand.

×1¼

$\times 2\frac{1}{2}$

$\times \frac{3}{4}$

The Striped Hawk-moth
Celerio livornica

This migrant hawk is a native of Africa but flies
north to Europe every year, occasionally in
prodigious numbers. In England it is only seen on
the wing at dusk and dawn, but in warmer climates
it flies during the day. There are many different
colour forms of the caterpillar.

×3

×1

The Silver-striped Hawk-moth
Hippotion celerio

This is a tropical moth, ranging through Africa and southern Asia as far as Australia. It has, however, a strong migratory instinct and often flies northwards through Europe. It is attracted to light and migrant specimens are often found on walls of houses, near lighted windows. The exotic-looking caterpillars feed mainly on grape-vine, but are seldom found in the northern parts of Europe.

Pyrenees. It occurs in Holland and Belgium, in the Rhine Valley and the Tyrol as well as on the Isle of Capri, where a particularly fine red form occurs. It is fairly widespread throughout France, especially in coastal districts, and I have myself found larvae in the forest of Fontainebleau.

The caterpillar of the Spurge Hawk is conspicuous in all its stages. Immediately after hatching it measures about 4 mm and is rather pale in colour but quickly darkens to almost black. When the larvae begin to feed they again become lighter, appearing greenish-black all over, except for the white spiracles. After they change their skins, at the end of the first week, the characteristic bold pattern appears on a greenish-yellow ground colour, and after the second moult the small raised white dots can be seen. The final instar is reached after about seventeen days and the larvae are usually ready to pupate four weeks after hatching from the egg.

As the caterpillars increase in size they become more and more spectacular and colourful and one must assume that they rely for protection on warning colours, rather than on any resemblance to the food plant. They are certainly very easily seen, both on the ground and while feeding, and they make no attempt at concealment. The Spurge Hawk larva is, in all its stages, a voracious feeder and does not move away from its food plant at all, even at night, but clings to the stems, clutching leaves and young shoots between its legs and literally stuffing them into its jaws. As Tutt says in his *British Lepidoptera*: 'Their lazy habits are beyond belief and their powers of eating extraordinary.'

The caterpillar begins to feed at the tip of the shoot, moving backwards down the stem as the leaves and faded flowers and even the stems themselves are consumed, until nothing is left but the thicker stalks. If it is disturbed, the larva swings its body from side to side and regurgitates a thick green fluid from its mouth.

Although it is sluggish while feeding, the Spurge Hawk caterpillar becomes very active just before pupating and will wander a considerable distance with remarkable speed. Before this restlessness begins the colours darken, so that it is no longer quite so conspicuous. When it finally decides to settle and spin a cocoon it does this more thoroughly than most of the other hawk-moths, weaving a fairly substantial structure of silk and sand, lined on the inside with smooth strands. The pupa is active and mobile. It is not at all unusual for individuals to lie over from one year to the next in the pupal stage. In southern Europe the moths begin to emerge in May and the second brood is on the wing during August and September.

The Spurge Hawk

The Spurge Hawk flies at dusk and again later during the night, coming to gardens to visit flowers, or feeding from wild plants in its native habitat. Sea campion is a favourite source of nectar. Mating takes place after dark and the pairs separate a couple of hours later, so they are never found together in the morning. The eggs, which number a hundred to a hundred and fifty, are laid over a period of a week or more.

The moth is variable and there are a number of distinct local forms as well as a great many named aberrations. Occasionally unusually large or small specimens are found and both ground colour and markings vary. In Spain there is a form in which the fore-wings are brightly flushed with pink.

The Bedstraw Hawk

CELERIO GALII

Haunts. The Bedstraw Hawk is, like the Spurge Hawk, much more common on the continent of Europe than in Britain, but it migrates with greater freedom and there are many records of both adult moths and larvae being found in the British Isles, especially in the west country, but also in many other places as far north as Carlisle; and it has also been found in Scotland. In Europe it is widespread, being found even in southern Sweden and Finland and breeding there, but it is doubtful whether pupae survive the winter so far north. The moth seems to favour areas with sandy soil, especially near the coast, and in Britain larvae are generally discovered among sandhills close to the beach, while the moths will come to feed from garden flowers.

The Egg. The bright green, rather small eggs measure about 1 mm across and are flattened, but almost circular in outline. They are laid, over a period, on the leaves or flowers of the white or yellow bedstraw (*Galium verum* and *Galium molugo*) and occasionally on willowherb (*Epilobium angustifolium*), or on fuchsia. They are often laid fairly close together, on adjoining sprigs of the food plant and hatch in anything from ten to eighteen days, depending on the weather. A well-fed female can lay anything up to four hundred eggs during her lifetime of three to four weeks.

The Caterpillar. The young larvae are at first light green but later darken in colour, and when fully fed they are dark olive, sometimes brownish, or occasionally almost black, with a paler line along the back. The underside of the body is a dull dark smoky pink. The head, and the dorsal plate just behind it, is also pinkish or mauve and the curved, rough tail is crimson. The skin is smooth, but distinctly subdivided into rings. Along each side of the body, above the spiracles, is a row of nine large round yellow spots, like port-holes on the side of a ship. The last spot is pear-shaped and joins with the base of the horn. On the segments just

77

behind the head are some quite small spots. Each spot is framed in black, which gradually merges with the ground colour. In the black form of the caterpillar the spots are less distinct, and often have dark centres. The spiracles are yellow, ringed with black. The caterpillar, when fully fed, measures some 8 cm in length and is thick and cylindrical in build, tapering towards the head, which is rather small. The skin is changed four times before pupation. On the Continent larvae are often parasitized by ichneumon flies but none of those found in Britain have ever been stung.

The Pupa. The pupa is sometimes just buried in the ground, but more often it lies on the surface, enclosed in a silken cocoon which binds together grains of sand and leaves of the food plant. It measures about 4 cm in length and is smooth and compact with a girth of $3\frac{1}{2}$ cm. The pupal skin is rather thin and easily injured, light brown at the head end and gradually darkening to a reddish-brown towards the dark curved anal spike. The wingcases, the head and the thorax are marked with fine black lines and the tongue and the antennae have a pale outline, so that they show up very distinctly. The moth sometimes emerges after only seventeen days, while others may remain in the pupal stage for over a year. On the Continent entomologists have found that usually those larvae which pupate before the middle of July will emerge after two or three weeks, while later ones overwinter as pupae. Specimens reared from caterpillars found in Britain in late summer seldom emerge, unless forced. In southern Europe the moth is normally double-brooded, but further north a single generation, with only occasional late summer individuals, is the rule.

The Adult Moth. The Bedstraw Hawk-moth, or Madder Hawk as the early fathers of entomology used to call it, may easily be mistaken for the Spurge Hawk, because superficially the moths are rather alike in colour as well as in pattern and general shape, although the Spurge Hawk is slightly more colourful. The main difference is in the markings of the fore-wings, which in the Bedstraw Hawk have a continuous area of olive-brown along the front margin. This dark band is indented and irregular along its lower edge, where it joins a creamy-yellow band. Below this is a wedge-shaped area of olive-brown followed by a grey band along the outer margin of the wing. The ground colour of the hind-wings is the same creamy yellow as the band on the fore-wing. The basal area is a very dark brown and there is a band of the same colour near the margin, edged with pale greyish-brown and fringed with white. The cream-coloured band is decorated with a rust-red patch followed by a white spot near the anal angle. The thorax and abdomen are olive-brown and so are the antennae. The abdomen is marked on either side with two thick black lines edged with white and there is a row of very small white spots along the central line on the upper surface. The joint between the wings and the thorax is marked with a fringe of fairly long white hairs. On the underside both pairs of wings are margined with grey, enclosing a dark cream coloured area with brown veins. The underside of the abdomen is barred with white. The body tapers to a sharp point, and except for the male having slightly longer and thicker antennae, there is no difference between the sexes.

Moses Harris, who figured the caterpillar of the Bedstraw Hawk-moth, called it The Spotted Elephant, which undoubtedly is a good name, because the first thing one notices about the fully fed larva is the row of spots, which are so bright that they look as if the creature is lit up from inside. Like its close relative the Spurge Hawk, the caterpillars of the Bedstraw Hawk vary a great deal in colour, and although they are not as gaudy, they are in their way just as striking, but do not assume their startling spots until the last instar.

The young caterpillar is a clear green with a yellow line along the centre of the back and two yellow lines along each side, one above and one below the spiracles. The upper one gradually begins to break up into sections, and at the final moult, which takes place when the caterpillar is still no more than half its ultimate size, the lines give way to spots. Immediately after this last skin change the caterpillar is almost black in colour, but after a couple of days it begins to fade, unless it happens to be one of the few which remain black throughout its life. The ground colouring may take on a yellowish-green, bottle-green or olive-green tinge, or even brown or grey. There is also a variation on the black type in which the body, except for a central line along the back, is thickly sprinkled with small bright yellow dots. The only constant feature is the colour of the bristly tail horn which almost invariably remains crimson. Occasionally specimens have been found with even the horn black and no stripes or spots whatsoever.

In Britain Bedstraw Hawk-moth caterpillars are usually found during September when they are nearly full-fed, and most of them have been found on bedstraw plants. In September 1943, five larvae were found on a patch of waste ground on the outskirts of Birmingham, feeding on willowherb in company with several Elephant Hawk larvae, just as they had been found ten years before in Berkshire, near Wellington College. Although the Bedstraw Hawk is not such a rarity in Britain as the Spurge Hawk, it is certainly only an occasional visitor and has been much rarer in the twentieth century than it was in the past. In the 1880s and '90s these moths came over in fair numbers and the summer of 1888 was a record year, in spite of bad weather, with nearly a thousand caterpillars collected, two hundred and fifty of them in Kent alone, and large numbers in Cheshire, Lancashire and Suffolk. Again in 1897 many were found on the sandhills at Wallasey, which appears to be a favourite haunt for these foreign visitors.

Coastal sandhills or areas of wasteland with plenty of bedstraw are, undoubtedly, the most likely places for immigrant Bedstraw Hawks to select as nurseries for their progeny, but apart from this, they have been found in many different places and even, on more than one occasion, in the Shetland Isles. The main reason why the moths do not seem to be able to establish themselves here, even after a very large migration, is probably the general lack of sunshine. The pupae can stand the cold winters in central Europe, but the damp, chilly autumns and wet winters of Britain cause too high a mortality.

Several observers have noticed that the caterpillars seem to like to bask in the full warmth of the sun, either right at the tops of rather small stunted plants where they are fully exposed, or actually on the sand, like people sunbathing on a beach. When they are touched, they behave in much the same way as Spurge Hawk caterpillars, jerking their bodies from side to side with quick violent movements and occasionally they even attempt to bite. In spite of their colouring they are not very obvious, and they can usually be tracked down most easily by their frass, which shows up clearly on the sand.

The Bedstraw Hawk-moth is a powerful flier, and stopping to feed on the way, it can cover long distances. In the south of Europe the moth is often seen on the wing in the daytime and it has also occasionally been noticed during daylight in this country, although normally it does not begin to fly here until dusk. The moth appears in spring and again later in the summer and most of those taken in Britain have been of the second brood, although there are a few records from last century, of moths taken here in May. They are attracted by light and in 1955 a number of specimens were caught in mercury vapour moth traps during July and August.

When larvae have been reared in captivity and the moths have emerged successfully, breeders have found that most of them are a good deal smaller than wild caught specimens, which are presumably migrants. This seems to indicate that some climatic factor inhibits their growth in this country, and it is unlikely that the Bedstraw Hawk could ever become established here as a native. The larvae apparently require sun and warmth to feed up satisfactorily and in cool weather they become sluggish and hide among leaves and debris at the foot of the food plant, as if trying to find a warm spot.

Although the caterpillars are so variable in colour, the adult moths differ much less, except in size. Sometimes the red spot on the hind-wings is reduced and the olive-brown areas on the wings may vary in outline and depth of colour, or be covered in grey scales. This form is known as aberration *grisea* and may well be an abnormal form caused by forcing the pupae in heat in captivity. Examples with incomplete wing bands have been taken and also a few gynandromorphs, but these are very rare.

The Striped Hawk

CELERIO LIVORNICA

Haunts. The Striped Hawk is a migrant, a native of Africa, but widespread throughout Europe in most seasons. It frequently reaches the British Isles, although seldom in large numbers. When these moths do arrive, at irregular intervals, they may be seen almost anywhere, but are naturally attracted by flowers, especially those which are scented, such as honeysuckle, valerian, petunias and others which provide plenty of nectar. Most of the records have been from coastal areas, where the moths first stop to feed after their Channel crossing.

The Egg. The eggs are pale green and are laid singly, on a variety of food plants. Larvae have been found on vine (*Vitis*), dock (*Rumex*), knotgrass (*Polygonum*), fuchsia, bedstraw (*Galium*), and snapdragon (*Antirrhinum*). The eggs hatch about three weeks after laying and each female is capable of laying over two hundred eggs.

The Caterpillar. The full-fed caterpillar is large, measuring 8 cm in length, and resembles in shape the larvae of the Spurge Hawk and the Bedstraw Hawk. The plump, firm, cylindrical body tapers towards the head, which is rather small, and the skin is smooth. The horn, which is almost straight, is reddish-yellow in colour with a blunt black tip. The ground colour of the body is a dark greenish-black marked with tiny yellow spots. The black head has a yellow streak across the mouth and the dorsal plate behind the head is black. Along the centre of the back, from the third segment to the horn, runs a pinkish-yellow stripe. Along the sides of the body run rather ill-defined yellowish lines, each interrupted by eight big pale yellow spots, slightly tinged with pink at the upper edge. Each spot is surrounded by a black ring and there are two black spots just above it. The spiracles are yellow with a pink tinge and below them runs an interrupted, rather puckered and swollen pale stripe. The underside of the body is dusky pink.

82

The Pupa. The larva spins a rather flimsy cocoon of silk threads and rubbish on the surface of the ground. The pupa, which is unusually long and somewhat flattened, measures over $4\frac{1}{2}$ cm from head to tail. It is thickest near the lower end of the wingcases, tapering towards head and tail. The anal horn is short and sharp. The head, which is narrow and clearly offset from the rest of the body, is ridged, like a helmet. The surface of the pupa is not glossy but very finely granulated, and the colour is a rather light brown with the last segments somewhat darker.

The Adult Moth. The Striped Hawk-moth is an elegant insect and takes its name from the distinct white veining on the fore-wings. The general ground colour of the fore-wings is olive-brown, interrupted by a creamy-pink line, which starts as a narrow streak near the apex of the wing and widens gradually towards the lower margin where it shades into pale grey. Along the outer margin runs a band of the same grey shade. The hind-wings are blackish-brown with a large central area of clear rosy pink, with a white spot near the inner margin. The thorax is olive-brown with fringes of white hair which look like the outline of a pair of short wings folded over the back. The abdomen is a slightly lighter olive-brown, banded with black and white and ends in pointed olive-brown tail tufts. The undersides of the wings are grey-brown, with irregular central areas of dull cream. The thorax and legs are grey-white on the underside and the abdomen golden brown, sprinkled with white. The antennae are thin and the same colour as the thorax, but whitish at the tips with re-curved brown bristles.

The Striped Hawk-moth is a true cosmopolitan, occurring all over Africa right down to the Cape, in Asia as far as India and northwards all over Europe and right into Siberia. A very closely related species, *Celerio lineata*, is found in North America where it is known as the Striped Morning Sphinx. The only difference in appearance is in the number of white stripes on the thorax.

This fine moth is not a true resident anywhere in Europe, except in the extreme south, but comes flying up from Africa in the spring, and although the females lay eggs on these journeys, the number of caterpillars found is rather small in comparison with the adult moths which have been recorded. In 1931, for example, which was an unusually good year for Striped Hawks in Britain, 142 moths were seen but only 28 larvae found. The earliest records of this moth in Britain go back to 1824, but unlike some of the other migrants which have not appeared in any numbers during this century, the Striped Hawk has been very prolific in Britain twice since the beginning of the twentieth century, in 1931 and again in 1943, which was an astonishing entomological year.

In that year, in the middle of the Second World War, the moths arrived in Britain at the end of May. The news flashed across the country from one entomologist to another almost faster than the moths could fly, and everywhere people were on the look-out for the migrants. Mr Guy Adkin, living at St Mawes in Cornwall, gave a very detailed account of his observations in *The Entomologist* and noted that the evening flight of these moths always took place for only a short period, between 8.45 and 9.30 G.M.T. and that after this brief feeding flight the moths disappeared and were not seen again until the following evening. An independent observer in east Kent confirmed this time of flight.

The greatest number of moths which Mr Adkin actually counted on any one night was 30, on 30th May and 5th June; the peak period lasted until 6th June, when there was a definite drop in numbers, and

×1

The Striped Hawk-moth is a very powerful insect and can fly incredible distances over land and water. Sometimes enormous swarms of these moths migrate through Europe in the summer, but they do not always get as far north as Britain.

after 28th June the moths vanished. An interesting point was that the disappearance of the moths coincided with an improvement in the weather, which had not been particularly good at the time when they were numerous. On 2nd June, when 11 moths were seen, the temperature was only 52°F. with a strong north-north-west wind and showers of rain, and generally the whole peak period was windy and cool.

While Mr Adkin in south Cornwall counted 208 moths, of which he captured 32, a friend of his, Col. Kershaw, saw 51 at Bude in north Cornwall and other entomologists in the same county brought the score to 280. Altogether about 500 were seen in Britain during that summer, and observers admitted that as they only counted the moths they could distinguish quite clearly and ignored any which were flying overhead or too far away to be properly identified, the actual number must have been far greater.

In 1949, when many Striped Hawks again appeared in Britain, further observations were made on their time of flight by Commander Harper at Rustington in Sussex where he counted over 100 between 26th August and 22nd September. He found that the moths flew, not only at dusk, but also in the early morning twilight, arriving at their favourite feeding place, a large bed of petunias, about forty minutes before sunrise while it was still too dark to see the flowers clearly, and half an hour later, before the sun actually rose above the horizon, they disappeared. Here again it was noted that strong winds and even showers of thundery rain did not deter the moths from feeding.

During the daytime the Striped Hawk does not normally fly in Britain, but settles to rest in some suitable place, and during this particular 'invasion' in Cornwall a number of moths were seen settled on the steep cliffs by a climber going down on a rope to inspect a kestrel's nest, and his observation was confirmed on the same day by a second rock climber who had also seen several moths settled.

The year 1946 was a record one for Striped Hawks on the continent of Europe, although not very many reached Britain. The tremendous migration started early in July when the moths were noticed in huge swarms in Algeria and they then moved up through Spain and crossed the Pyrenees into France. They were seen in enormous numbers in Andorra on 22nd July and were still there in force a fortnight later. They flew on northwards, swarming all over the south of France and Switzerland and continued up into Germany, a few even reaching Holland and Sweden. Experienced Swiss naturalists were afraid to say how many they had seen in case they were thought to be making a gross exaggeration, but when pressed they admitted that the moths had not come only in hundreds, or even thousands, but literally in millions, and could be seen, especially in the high Alpine valleys, hovering close together over the flowers, not only at dawn and dusk, but all day long, as if they were unable to appease their hunger for nectar. They were seen as high as four thousand metres (twelve thousand feet) and appeared to be on the move from south to north. On 12th August the temperature suddenly dropped sharply and the moths disappeared, but nothing like it had been experienced since 1818, when similar swarms of Striped Hawks had been noted.

This remarkable migration confirmed many interesting facts about this strange moth. It was again noticed that in Africa, Spain and southern France, where the sunlight is hot and strong, the moths were invariably on the wing at all hours of the day, flying both in sunlight and also on days when the sky was overcast. Further north they tend to be seen in greater numbers at dusk, although even in central France, and certainly in Switzerland, they also fly in the daytime. In Britain practically all the records of Striped Hawks on the wing have been at dawn or dusk, but on a few occasions they have been seen flying along the sea shore in daylight, as at Littlehampton on 12th July 1945 when a dozen were noticed on the beach at ten o'clock in the morning and in 1946 when one was reported 'probing at the straw on the sunny side of a stack at 7.15 in the morning'. Possibly all these moths were migrants which had only just arrived. The explanation for this difference in behaviour is probably that in the south the moths habitually fly during the day, but this habit is retained further north only while they are still in the grip of the migratory urge; once their desire to move onwards has spent itself they settle down to rest during the day and feed only at dawn and dusk, possibly because they need less food in a cooler climate when they are no longer so active.

Although, in 1946, it was reported that thousands upon thousands of caterpillars of the Striped Hawk moth had been killed as pests in Andalusia, the enormous swarms which continued their journey north-wards beyond the Pyrenees apparently left no progeny. A number of females were caught and examined in Germany and nearly all of them proved to be infertile. A few, however, did lay eggs, but all the larvae died at an early age of the wilt disease known in France as 'flacherie'. The fact that the females of late summer migrations are often sterile has been noted before in Britain but so far the reason for this has not been explained. In the case of females arriving in the spring, however, it is usually a different story, and when larvae have been found they have obviously been the progeny of early migrants, which have arrived in May or June. Very fresh moths taken in the late summer are also almost certainly the descendants of spring migrants, because those moths which have flown across the Channel are invariably somewhat worn. Occasionally very fresh and rather worn specimens have been caught in what appears to be the same swarm, indicating that a migration from the Continent has coincided with the emergence of home-bred moths.

The great variety of unrelated food plants on which the Striped Hawk-moth caterpillars have been found is particularly interesting and unusual, as most Hawk-moth larvae are restricted in their choice or confine themselves to plants of the same botanical family, while these will eat almost anything. In 1931 a lady found eleven big caterpillars stripping the leaves off the snapdragons in her garden in Kent. Not being an entomologist she destroyed six of them before her son arrived and managed to rescue five and from these four moths were bred out. Other larvae have been discovered feeding on fuchsias, dock, sorrel and bedstraw and also in fields of mangel wurzels. On 20th July 1943 Mr Guy Adkin found five caterpillars on a patch of buckwheat at St Mawes. They were obviously the progeny of a spring migrant of that year. All the larvae were of the black form and all pupated, but only two emerged, both perfect males, one a good deal larger than the other.

In southern Europe the caterpillars are often found on vines and during the summer of 1943 some British officers, who were held as prisoners of war in a villa near Abruzzi in Italy, amused themselves by rearing a large brood of larvae, which they obtained from eggs laid by some female moths they had captured and confined in a bucket with a bunch of vine leaves. The caterpillars proved easy to rear and the second generation emerged in the middle of July. In Britain, on the whole, the Striped Hawk-moth has been rather difficult in captivity even on vines grown under glass and it is possible that this may be due to lack of direct sunlight. Considering their native habitat, it is very likely that the caterpillars need plenty of sun to develop properly and the pupae also probably require warmth. In one instance, however, recorded in *The Entomologist* in 1944, a moth which pupated in the summer of 1943 and was then subjected to a temperature of up to 100°F. during the autumn, refused to emerge, but eventually did so in September 1944 after spending the rest of the winter and all the following summer in a cool room.

When it first hatches, the young caterpillar is a dirty white, with a black head and horn. It is the only European hawk-moth to have a black head in the first instar. Some days after beginning to feed it darkens in colour, becoming first green and then almost black after the first moult. Very often the skin is thickly dotted with small yellow spots, which give the larva a greenish appearance, but fully fed specimens are also sometimes a rich dark green in ground colour and the fine dots may be entirely missing. Sometimes the spots along either side are also lacking and the stripe along the back is very variable. The only caterpillar of this moth which I myself have ever reared had a broad black line with a transverse black bar on each segment, which gave the appearance of a series of black crosses along the back. These cross bands ended with a small crescent-shaped cluster of pale yellowish-white dots, which were part of a yellow line along the side, but there were no distinct round spots at all. Larvae with yellow or green stripes along the back have also been described, and the underside of the body varies considerably in colour, from almost whitish to dark plum, or nearly black.

In Europe the larvae usually hatch in June and feed up fairly quickly, so that they are ready to pupate in the middle of July or at the beginning of August. Further south, as for example in Sicily, the first-brood larvae pupate by the end of June and emerge again as adults three weeks later. Hardly any of the caterpillars found in England and successfully reared have remained in the pupal stage for more than a month. South of the Mediterranean the Striped Hawk is continuously brooded throughout the year, usually producing three generations and spending the months of November, December and January in the pupal stage. In Europe the moth appears to be resident only in the southern half of Spain and Italy and in Malta and although it can breed during the summer further north the pupae do not survive the winter.

The sexes are almost identical, except that the females tend to be slightly larger than the males and have smaller and thinner antennae. Specimens differ in the intensity of their colouring, but the main variation is in the width of the dark areas on the hind-wings. Sometimes these are unusually wide, making the entire wing much darker than normal. The bands on the fore-wings also vary in width and depth of colouring, although more rarely, and individual moths show considerable difference in size, irrespective of sex.

The Silver-striped Hawk

HIPPOTION CELERIO

Haunts. This is another migrant hawk-moth, a native of Africa and southern Asia, ranging as far as Australia, but it appears fairly regularly in southern Europe along the Mediterranean coast, and from there wanders northwards. In the British Isles it has been found over most of England and Wales and even in Scotland, and it has also appeared in Ireland. There are no special localities for the moth in Britain, but most of the specimens have been found in the southern counties and especially in Devonshire.

The Egg. The eggs are rather small and clear green, but change to a dull yellow before hatching. They are not round but somewhat pointed at either end and are fixed on the leaves of the food plant, either vine, virginia creeper, fuchsia or bedstraw, both on the upper and the under surface. Each female is said to be capable of laying about three hundred eggs if well fed.

The Caterpillar. The full-grown caterpillars vary in appearance and may be either green or brown, often a very dark, almost blackish-brown, which is more common than the green colouring. They are long, measuring some 8 or even 9 cm, fairly slender and tapering very noticeably towards the small head which is drawn back into the fourth segment when the larva is resting, rather in the same way as the Elephant Hawk retracts the front segments of its body. The head itself is brown and the tail short, straight and almost black, with a glossy tip. A pale line runs along each side from the head to the tail horn. It is wider on the first three segments than on the rest of the body and on segments four and five it is interrupted by round eye-spots. The first of these is large and prominent and consists of a round black spot with either a centre of white dots or a single white pupil set a little to one side. It is surrounded by a ring of yellow with an outer margin of black. The second spot is somewhat smaller and less vividly marked. The dark ring round the edge may be missing. The spiracles are creamy white ringed with black and there are small red spots immediately above them. A dull yellow stripe runs just above the true legs on the fore part of the body. The back is marked with fine black lengthways streaks. In the green form of the caterpillar the eye-spots are more silvery than yellow and the longitudinal stripe is simply a paler shade of the ground colour. Before pupating the caterpillar becomes a very dark purplish-brown.

The Pupa. The caterpillar usually burrows down into the ground an inch or more, but sometimes pupates on the surface among dead leaves, making a very slight silken cocoon. The pupa is a light brown in colour, very like that of the Oleander Hawk, but it has more extensive black markings on the wingcases and on the underside of the body. The black spots round the spiracles are smaller. In outline the pupa is very smooth and tapering. The tongue is not separate but enclosed in a keel-like projection which is very noticeable on the head of the pupa. It measures about $4\frac{1}{2}$ cm in length. The moth spends only a short time in the pupal stage, normally emerging three or four weeks after pupating.

The Adult Moth. The Silver-striped Hawk-moth is a beautiful and striking insect, although not very large. It measures about 7 cm across the wings and has a slim body not much more than $3\frac{1}{2}$ cm long ending in a thin, pointed tail tuft, and with its narrow, slightly hooked wings it gives an impression of speed. The fore-wings are light brown with a silvery streak running from the tip in a slight curve to the hind margin of the wing, near the base. Alongside this line run other lines of dark and light brown and the wing is edged with a narrow band of lavender-grey. The upper part of the wing is marked with a few rather short, silvery streaks. The hind-wings are a rich rosy red near the body, the colour fading and merging into light brown towards the edge, and this paler area is patterned with a 'trellis' of black veins, joined near the edge by a black line. The thorax and abdomen are a soft brown colour with a lavender-grey streak edged with paler lines running down the centre of the back. On either side of this, on the thorax, is a short golden streak followed by a band of silvery white, stretching from the eye to the base of the hind-wings. On either side of the abdomen are some small white dashes; the enormous eyes are dark brown and the rather slender antennae a very pale brown, becoming lighter towards the tips. The undersides of the fore-wings are a dull sandy colour with darker flecks and faint rusty patches adjoining the darker brown basal area. The hind-wings are a lighter sandy tint with a faint suggestion of pink showing through from the upper side. The legs and the underside of the body are putty-coloured.

When the Silver-striped Hawk-moth does come to Britain, and that is not very often, it is almost invariably a late visitor, arriving in August, September or October when any possibility of breeding is ruled out. In its tropical habitat in Africa and India it has three generations or sometimes even four in a year, in the southernmost parts of Europe two, but even there it is not a true native and if reinforcements did not arrive across the Mediterranean the moth would probably disappear. Very occasionally some of the early summer individuals reach Britain and, if they can find any vines, lay a few eggs here, but the migrants which arrive in the autumn are almost invariably sterile.

The years 1884 and 1885, when one was found on Blackfriar's Bridge, were good years for the Silver-striped Hawk in Britain, and so was 1892, but in the present century the moths have been very much scarcer, with an average of not more than one moth a year actually recorded. In 1938 and again twenty years later in 1958 the score was five moths seen and identified beyond doubt and in late October 1963 two or three were noted, but the chances of finding a Silver-striped Hawk-moth in Britain are very small.

The moths which have been picked up in the past have very often been discovered on the walls of houses, close to lighted windows, which apparently attracted them during the night, and although this is a moth which has a long tongue and feeds on nectar, comparatively few have been caught at flowers, possibly because by the time they arrive here most of the flowers which are rich in nectar are over. The moth does not appear only in one part of Britain and has been found in practically every English county as well as in Scotland, but there are only a few records from Ireland. On the whole the south-eastern districts, both north and south of the Thames, are most favoured, as one might expect with a migrant moth arriving from the Continent.

In southern Spain Silver-striped Hawks are often very common in the early autumn and can be seen feeding from the blue plumbago in the early evening. Like most of the other hawk-moths they seem to have a set time—only about half an hour—for feeding, and after this they disappear. Their flight is extremely rapid and when disturbed the moths vanish in a flash.

The larvae are naturally even rarer than the adult moths in Britain, but they have been found, occasionally even four or five of them together. In their native habitat they feed on vine (*Vitis*) or virginia creeper (*Ampelopsis*) and in southern Europe the vineyards are the places to search for larvae, or perhaps more profitably odd vines growing in corners where they are not sprayed. The young larvae are green at first with very long tail horns. In the second instar the eye-spots begin to show as faint dark marks and in the third they become well defined and surrounded by dark rings. At this time also the change to brown occurs in those which are of the dark type.

Like the Elephant Hawk, the caterpillar retracts its head when alarmed or while resting between periods of feeding and this accentuates the spots, which no doubt have a protective value. In north Africa and the Middle East, where the moth is common, the caterpillars are very often found on vines growing on the fronts of houses or over walls. They will also eat fuchsia and bedstraw. In Queensland, Australia, the moth is very common, breeding all the year round, and it has the same habit in India.

Contrary to the general rule among hawk-moths, the female Silver-striped Hawk is usually slightly smaller than the male, with a shorter body and shorter antennae, but apart from this the sexes are alike. Tropical specimens are often a good deal larger and richer in colouring than those reared further north, and individuals differ in the shape and intensity of the silver streak, the depth of colouring of the hind-wing and the size of the white flecks on the abdomen.

The Hummingbird Hawk

MACROGLOSSA STELLATERUM

Haunts. This delightful little hawk-moth can be seen absolutely anywhere and is not confined to any particular place or type of country; it has even on many occasions been seen hovering around ships at sea. It is very common in the south of Europe and regularly flies northwards, reaching all the Scandinavian countries and Finland. It flies all over Russia and is seen on the high Alpine passes and in busy city streets. It often reaches Britain, travelling right up to the Shetlands, and as it appears to have no fear of humans or of motor traffic it comes to parks and gardens and flower stalls, wherever there is a chance of finding nectar.

The Egg. The egg is green and spherical but slightly taller than it is broad, measuring about 1 mm in height. Under a magnifying glass it can be seen that the surface is slightly pitted, but to the naked eye it appears smooth. The eggs are laid singly among the buds or flowers of bedstraw (*Galium*) and also on valerian (*Kenthrantus*). They hatch within seven or eight days of laying. A female can lay anything up to two hundred eggs.

The Caterpillar. The caterpillars of the Hummingbird Hawk feed up very quickly, reaching their full size in three weeks if the weather is warm and they have ample food. In the last instar the caterpillar measures $4\frac{1}{2}$ cm in length. It is rather stout, tapering from the fifth segment towards the small round head. The body ends in a short straight horn with a sharp point. There are two distinct colour forms, one green, the other brown. Along the back runs a broad band of a deeper shade than the rest of the body and there is nearly always a pale, almost whitish line along each side, from the second segment to the tail. Below the spiracles, just above the legs, runs a narrow yellow line, but this is sometimes missing in the dark caterpillars. Each segment is subdivided into eight sections by folds in the skin, which is covered in tiny rough white points. The horn is nearly always blueish, with a touch of yellow at the tip. Before pupating the fully fed larvae turn a reddish-purple colour.

The Pupa. The pupa is normally enclosed in a rather flimsy silk cocoon, spun either among the leaves of the food plant or amongst rubbish on the ground, incorporating grains of sand or soil and dead leaves in the structure. It measures some 3 to $3\frac{1}{2}$ cm in length and is a pale reddish-brown in colour, marked with dark brown, especially on the wingcases and spiracles. The prominent tongue case is flattened from the sides and the body ends in a straight sharp spike with two spines. During the summer the moth emerges three weeks after pupating, so the whole sequence from egg to adult is completed in two months.

The Adult Moth. The Hummingbird Hawk-moth is comparatively small, measuring not more than about 5 cm in wing-span and with a body length of just under 3 cm. The fore-wings are a soft dark grey, slightly mottled in effect and crossed by two wavy dark bands which run from the front margin to the hind margin of the wing. The hind-wings are orange, with a grey area at the base and a narrow brown margin. The thorax is covered in thick grey hair, the same colour as the fore-wings. The abdomen too is grey but turns black at the tip and is marked on either side with a creamy white patch. The body ends in a thick double tuft of black hair which is spread out fanwise in flight. The antennae are dark grey, thickening towards the tip, and end in a curved bristle. On the underside the wings are dull yellow at the base, shading into reddish-brown and then to a dull brown at the edges. The abdomen is surrounded by a black and white fringe, the thorax and palpi are greyish-white and this colour also extends to and surrounds the golden brown, large eyes. The long tongue is rolled up between the palpi when not in use.

No other moth enjoys such universal popularity as the Hummingbird Hawk and even the superstitious peasants of Italy and Malta, who regard the Death's-head as an evil omen, welcome the Hummingbird Hawk in their houses as a messenger of good will and happy tidings. Its obvious harmlessness and the way it seems to like and seek out human habitations and gardens throughout the sunny hours and its strange bird-like appearance, enhanced by the long tongue which resembles a slender curved beak, have all combined to make it a well-loved insect. Edward Newman's classic description gives a vivid mental picture of the moth: 'What is this, at our jasmine, with bird-like head, with brilliant eye, with outspread and parti-coloured tail, humming loudly, and, though

94

driven away, returning again and again, day after day, from the rising to the setting of the sun? It is the Hummingbird Hawk-moth—from January to December we have some flower to welcome her and she is welcome, most welcome to us and ours.'

Jasmine certainly seems to be the favourite flower of the Hummingbird Hawk, but it will visit blooms of every kind, from primroses and violets to geraniums, lilacs, verbenas and even the dangerous subtropical climber *Araujia sericofera*, which frequently traps a moth by its tongue so that it hangs helpless and struggling from the flower until it dies or breaks off its delicate proboscis in its efforts to escape. Mrs V. M. Muspratt, who lived for many years at St Jean de Luz in southern France, reported tragedies of this kind in a letter to *The Entomologist*. Seeing a Hummingbird Hawk fluttering for an unusually long time in front of one particular flower she went to investigate and found the moth trapped in this way. She managed to release it by cutting the flower with a sharp penknife, and afterwards when she examined this sinister plant she found one dead moth hanging by its tongue, and four flowers each containing a broken proboscis. Subsequently, on the same plant, she discovered four more dead moths and eleven broken tongues, but managed to rescue three moths which were still alive.

Hummingbird Hawk-moths are often seen in town gardens during the spring and summer, and in the second week of April 1948 a lady living in a flat on the top floor of a high block in Kensington, London, was amazed to see a Hummingbird Hawk feeding from the primulas in her window box above the main street. Hers were the only flowers within sight and the moth was obviously hungry, visiting each flower in turn and staying about twenty minutes before it disappeared. Another observer in London had a Hummingbird Hawk come regularly every day for nearly a fortnight at the same time in the afternoon, to a box of petunias, indicating that the moth must have had both a memory and a sense of time and was obviously a resident in the area.

Although the Hummingbird Hawk flies in brilliant sunshine, it also flies both at dusk and after dark and quite often too in the pouring rain or on dull cool days. Such an active insect naturally needs plenty of food and is always investigating all kinds of coloured objects, in case they might yield some nectar. Hummingbird Hawks have been noticed hovering in front of highly polished brass door knobs, around the painted tops of croquet sticks, inspecting gaily coloured posters or artificial flowers or trying in vain to get into greenhouses where they could see exotic orchids through the glass.

The Hummingbird Hawk

On several occasions these little moths have come to extract nectar from a buttonhole flower or a bouquet carried in the hand and at Nice and Cannes they are often seen round the baskets and stalls of the flower markets. They also have a curious habit, which has been noticed again and again, but never really explained, of hovering up and down in front of bare stone or brick walls, where they can find neither nectar nor food plants for egg laying. It has been suggested that they do this because they enjoy the warmth given off by the wall, while other observers have put forward the theory that the moths are looking for cracks and crevices

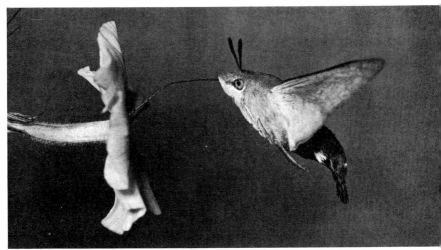

The Hummingbird Hawk-moth feeds on the wing, probing deep into the flowers with its long tongue. It often visits window boxes in towns or hovers round the baskets in the flower markets. It is not at all shy and occasionally comes into houses to hibernate in the autumn.

where they can hide and rest. In very hot weather, in the south of Europe, they certainly seem to take a 'siesta' of some hours during the hottest part of the day, often under the coping at the top of a wall, and resume their feeding flights again later when the temperature has fallen.

While feeding, the Hummingbird Hawk-moth seems almost oblivious of its surroundings, and it is possible to get very close. I even know of somebody who caught several specimens for breeding by imprisoning them between two jam jars while they were flying in front of flowers.

In the south the Hummingbird Hawk-moth has at least three, and possibly four broods in the year and goes into a state of semi-hibernation during mid-winter, hiding away in nooks and crannies, but especially among old clothes, which for some reason seem to hold a special attraction for the insect. Major C. S. Jarvis, writing in *Country Life* about his memories of these moths in Egypt, said: 'Against the Hummingbird Hawk-moth I have no great complaint except that he selected invariably one's wardrobe for his hibernating quarters. One saw them in the autumn buzzing round pictures, curtains and other mural hangings, but none of these ever found favour in their eyes, as what they were looking for was a pair of breeches, a shirt, or an old coat. Until one has become accustomed to the experience, a lively Hummingbird Hawk-moth, doing his hovering business with violently vibrating wings in the region of the small of one's back, is a very alarming experience. One thinks instinctively of horned vipers, scorpions and tarantulas and never suspects the quite harmless and most attractive little Hummingbird Hawk-moth.'

But in spite of this predilection for the comfortable folds and texture of human clothing, these little moths will also hibernate in other places, and after a broadcast some years ago I had a letter from a lady in Devonshire who had discovered one of these moths snugly installed for the winter behind a thick volume in her bookcase, and they have certainly been found on several occasions in dark corners, both indoors and in garden sheds. A couple of years ago my sons reported seeing a Hummingbird Hawk in the autumn, inspecting the hot-water pipes running through a corridor in their school at Ramsgate, no doubt searching for suitable winter quarters. A specimen taken in the hallway of a block of offices in the centre of Bristol on 22nd February 1950 was also, almost certainly, a hibernator which had just woken up, and other records from March and April are probably of the same nature.

Until very recently I did not know if the moths paired before or after hibernation when bred in England, but during the long hot summer of 1964 a young friend, Peter Hobbs, bred a small brood of these moths from a female captured in a garden in Wells, Somerset, early that summer. From the resulting progeny one pair of moths mated in a breeding cage during August. The female, however, died within a few days without depositing any eggs, although she was given growing food plant and an ample supply of flowers, from which she could feed and obtain nourishment.

Personally I have never seen a pair in copula and can find only one very old record, nearly a hundred years old, when a pair were seen flying across a path at Gibraltar. The mating, almost certainly, only lasts a short time. The female lays her eggs on the wing, without settling, although she does cling to the food plant with her legs, her wings vibrating strongly all the time, while she bends her body down and fixes the egg among the buds at the top of the plant. Before laying she appears to examine the sprig carefully, possibly to ascertain whether there are already other eggs laid upon it, and usually one finds only a single egg laid on a flower head. The egg is nearly always fixed to an unopened bud, which it closely resembles, and it is not at all easy to find.

Few entomological books mention valerian as a food plant, but in July 1948 Mr Clifford Crauffurd actually watched a female Hummingbird Hawk laying on the seed heads of this plant. He succeeded in finding two of the eggs, which hatched in five days, and reared the larvae. The following year another entomologist in Devonshire also observed a female ovipositing on valerian, which must therefore be considered as one of the normal food plants.

The short life cycle is remarkable, and the newly hatched caterpillars, which are a clear yellow colour and almost cylindrical in shape, begin to eat voraciously almost at once, and change their skins for the first time four days later. In the second instar they are green, with tiny yellow shagreen dots, each one, if seen under a magnifying glass, carrying a small black double-tipped bristle. The tail horn is purplish-red. A darker green line, formed by the absence of the yellow spots, runs along the centre of the back, and along the side is a narrow yellow line ending at the tail. The third instar is much the same in general appearance. In the final skin the tapering of the body becomes more obvious, the horn turns blue and the colour may be either predominantly green or brown. The final colour change to purplish-brown just before pupating is naturally not as noticeable in the brown as in the green form of the larva.

The Hummingbird Hawk-moth never remains long in the pupa. The moths invariably emerge again in the autumn and have been seen even in Britain in late November and again on sunny days in January and February, but it is very doubtful whether many moths actually survive here the whole winter, and if they do, the chances of them reproducing themselves are very slender indeed. The moths seen in Britain are therefore nearly always migrants or the descendants of migrants which have arrived here in the spring and early summer. Migrations during May have often been recorded. The moths have been observed in large numbers at sea-side resorts and there are many reports of them having been seen at sea, hovering around ships and settling on the rigging, or appearing for a few moments only and then flying off again across the water. One of the most dramatic reports of this kind was the observation made by a member of the Armed Forces crossing to France on D-day. Far out in the Channel he saw a small swarm of Humming-bird Hawks flying over the water on their way to England, while he, with thousands of his fellows, was preparing to invade the country they had just left.

The number of Hummingbird Hawk-moths reaching Britain varies greatly from year to year, but almost every summer at least a few of them are seen. In some seasons they come in enormous numbers and usually they are most numerous in the early autumn, during September. In good years many larvae are picked up in suitable localities, especially near the coast and one summer my father and I gathered some two hundred feeding on bedstraw along the beach near Walmer in Kent. 1959 was a good year with nearly 800 moths recorded, the first one seen in the middle of February at Seaford in Sussex and the last found in a house at Bradford in Yorkshire, on 3rd December. In 1960 only 132 moths were actually reported to the Insect Immigration Committee, and in 1958 a mere 90 were recorded.

In spite of its enormous range the Hummingbird Hawk-moth varies very little in appearance. Unusually small specimens are sometimes captured, but apart from a slight difference in the colour of the hind-wings, the moths are generally all identical. Very pale, albinistic specimens have very occasionally been found, and also some having the hind-wings entirely blackish-brown. There is hardly any difference between the sexes, but the females are slightly larger and stouter in the body and have smaller and thinner antennae than the males.

Celerio nicaea

Haunts. This is a hawk-moth which normally only occurs in southern Europe and only once have two larvae been found in Britain. The moth is rather rare, even in its native haunts, but may be found in Spain, southern France, Italy, Greece and Yugoslavia.

The Egg. The green eggs are normally laid on species of spurge (*Euphorbia*) and many different kinds have been noted as food plants of the larvae. On the occasion when caterpillars were found in Britain, they were feeding on toadflax (*Linaria vulgaris*).

The Caterpillar. The fully fed caterpillar is very remarkable in appearance and cannot very well be confused with any other species of Hawk-moth. It is large (nearly 12 cm in length) and rather slender, a pale grey in colour and marked with rows of round yellow spots, bordered by thick, irregular bands of black. The head is pale with black markings and the rough tail horn is also black.

The Pupa. The pupa measures 5 cm in length and is a pale yellowish-brown with the limbs and antennae outlined in black. It lies on the surface of the ground, among leaves, in a rather flimsy cocoon of yellow silk, intermingled with leaves and rubbish. The two larvae found in Britain on 20th August 1954 overwintered as pupae and the moths emerged on 12th July 1955.

The Adult Moth. The moth closely resembles the Spurge Hawk, but the spot on the inner edge of the hind-wing, which is creamy white in the Spurge Hawk, is reddish in *nicaea* and the transverse band on the fore-wing reaches the inner edge nearer the margin. This is not normally a migrant hawk and it is possible that the female which laid its eggs in Devon in 1954 had come to Britain across the Bay of Biscay on board a ship.

The Oak Hawk

MARUMBA QUERCUS

Haunts. This fairly large moth, which in many ways resembles the Poplar Hawk, is a southern European insect. It occurs along the Mediterranean coast of Spain, France and Italy, extending its range from here to lower Austria and eastwards to Caucasia and Mesopotamia. It is found in wooded hilly regions where oak trees grow.

The Egg. The pale green eggs are large and broadly oval and are laid singly on the underside of oak leaves, usually on the cork oak (*Quercus suber*), but the larvae will also eat common oak. The female moths select for preference young shrubby oaks, rather than big old trees.

The Caterpillar. The larva is very variable in shades of green, yellow or yellowish-green or even blue and is sometimes sprinkled with very fine yellow dots. It is difficult to find in the wild as it is well camouflaged amongst the foliage of the cork oaks. The sides of the body are marked with seven oblique yellow stripes, alternately broader and narrower, and the tail horn is blue. The head, which tapers into two points, is green with a yellow band along the edge. The larvae feed on the undersides of the leaves and are very inconspicuous owing to their disruptive colouring, the body shape being broken up by the slanting yellow stripes. Before pupating they turn a reddish-brown and then leave the trees during the night or very early in the morning. There is only one generation a year. Plenty of direct sunlight is essential for the well-being of the larvae and they are therefore difficult to rear in captivity, unless the cage can be stood in the full sun. The pupation period is during August and September.

The Pupa. The pupa is a rich reddish-brown with a rough tail spike with a double point. Before pupating the larva constructs a large cocoon from particles of earth cemented together, and unless the soil is of the light, gritty kind found along the Mediterranean coast, the caterpillars do not appear to be able to pupate satisfactorily and there is heavy mortality. Sand or clay soil has been found useless in captivity.

The Adult Moth. The Oak Hawk-moth emerges over rather a long period, from the beginning of June until well into July. It is rather larger than the Poplar Hawk-moth although similar in shape, but instead of being grey it is a pale ochreous colour. A lighter band, with dark edges, runs across the fore-wings and the hind-wings are shaded with orange-brown. The body is slightly darker than the wings. The antennae are rather long and tapering. On the underside the body and wings are more or less uniform pale buff. The females measure about 2 cm more across the wings than the males, and have much thicker bodies. When resting, the moths hold their wings in much the same attitude as the Lime Hawk-moth, and not like the Poplar Hawk-moth, with the hind-wings showing in front of the fore-wings. The mating flight takes place at dusk but the moths usually part before the morning.

Celerio vespertilio

Haunts. This moth has never been recorded in Britain and it is not a migrant species. It occurs in southern Europe, from the south of France through Switzerland, Bavaria and Austria eastwards to the Caucasus, but has never been found in Spain. It is local in its distribution, fairly common some years in certain localities, but not generally widespread, and usually prefers dry ground on mountain sides.

The Egg. The eggs are apple green, oval and slightly flattened. They are laid, very often in pairs, on the undersides of the leaves of *Epilobium rosemarininifolium*.

The Caterpillar. The caterpillar is at first green and in the later stages normally grey-brown and rather like the larva of the Elephant Hawk in general colouring. Each segment bears a pair of prominent spots on either side, usually red in colouring and edged with black. The larva has no tail horn in any stage of its development. When young, the caterpillars remain on the food plants both day and night, but after the second moult they become nocturnal in their habits, hiding among the lowest leaves or even among rubbish and stones on the ground during the day, crawling up again to feed at dusk.

The Pupa. The caterpillar pupates at ground level, among leaves and rubbish, inside a flimsy silk cocoon. The pupa is slim in outline and of a light brown colour. In the lower valleys the moth is partially double-brooded, with a second generation appearing in August and September, but at higher altitudes the first generation often does not emerge until July and there is no second brood.

The Adult Moth. The moth is about the same size as the Spurge Hawk and of a similar shape. The fore-wings are an almost uniform blue-grey, with only very faint darker markings. The hind-wings are a soft red with a dark-grey band along the edge and a touch of black at the base. The body is grey, marked with black and white along the sides. The antennae are white and the underside corresponds to the upper surface but is paler and more subdued.

Celerio hippophaes

Haunts.   This is rather a rare moth, occurring in Spain and from there distributed northwards through southern France and Switzerland to southern Germany, but nowhere is it common.

The Egg.   The green eggs are laid on the leaves of sea buckthorn (*Hippophae rhamnoides*).

The Caterpillar.   The full-fed caterpillar, which measures $7\frac{1}{2}$ to 8 cm in length, is a pale grey-green in colour. The front part of each segment of the body is a somewhat darker blue-green, giving the effect of a series of bands round the body. A rather indistinct yellow line runs along each side and ends in an elongated orange-yellow spot which joins up with the thin tail horn, which is the same colour. The head is greyish and a fairly broad white line runs the length of the body beneath the brown spiracles. When they are approaching their full size the larvae like to sun themselves on the topmost branches of the shrubs, where their colouring blends well with the grey-green foliage and the orange berries.

The Pupa.   The pupa, which is enclosed in a flimsy web among debris on the ground beneath the food plant, is a rather light grey-brown in colour, marked with darker streaks.

The Adult Moth.   At first glance the moth appears to be very like the Spurge Hawk, but the fore-wings are of a more general greyish tint with a brown band running from just below the apex and widening towards the inner margin of the wing. Between this band and the outer edge the wing is grey, and above it buff coloured with a darker olive-brown shading along the front edge and an elongated dark median spot. The basal area of the fore-wing, close to the body, is also a dark sepia-brown.

$\times \frac{1}{3}$

$\times \frac{3}{4}$

*The Hummingbird
Hawk-moth*
Macroglossa stellaterum

*Often mistaken for a
small exotic bird, this
charming little hawk-moth
flies both in the sunshine
and at dusk, in its search
for nectar. It is the only
species which hibernates
as an adult. The
caterpillars may be brown
or green and can be
found on bedstraw or
valerian.*

$\times 1\frac{3}{4}$

Celerio nicaea

*There is only one
record of this moth
reaching England; in
1954 two caterpillars
were found in Devon
feeding on toadflax
and successfully
reared.*

$\times 1\frac{1}{4}$

×1½

×¾

The Oak Hawk-moth
Marumba quercus

This large moth bears
a close resemblance to the
Poplar Hawk. It occurs
along the Mediterranean
coast of Spain, France
and Italy. The
caterpillars can be found
feeding on cork oak and
common oak in the hilly
regions close to the sea.

×2

Celerio vespertilio

*This moth has never been recorded as
far north as Britain, but it is fairly
common in southern and central Europe.
At high altitudes it is only single-
brooded, but in the lower valleys there
is a partial second brood in August and
September. This species has been
extensively used in hybridizing
experiments.*

×1

$\times 1\frac{3}{4}$

Celerio hippophaes

*At first glance this moth might be mistaken
for a Spurge Hawk, but it is a much rarer
insect found only in rather restricted localities
in southern and central Europe. The caterpillar
feeds on the leaves of sea buckthorn and is
grey-green with a single orange spot near the
tail horn.*

×3

Proserpinus proserpina

This distinctive moth is found locally from central Germany southwards to the Mediterranean and also in Spain and Portugal.

A mercury vapour moth trap working at night in the author's garden in Kent.

×2¼

Hemaris croatica

This colourful moth is closely related to the Bee Hawks, but unlike these it does not have transparent wings. It is found only in the south-eastern parts of Europe.

The hind-wings are pale red, edged with dark brown and with a dark brown shading at the base. The antennae are pale cream and the body dark olive with two square black spots on either side. The moth is normally single-brooded, appearing in early summer, but occasionally a few second-brood specimens emerge in August.

Proserpinus proserpina

Haunts. This rather rare hawk-moth, which differs distinctly in appearance from all the other species, is found from central Germany southwards to the Mediterranean and also in parts of Spain and Portugal.

The Egg. The egg is rather small and clear green, and is laid on species of *Epilobium*, *Lythrum* or *Oenothera*.

The Caterpillar. The larva is slender and cylindrical in shape, measuring some 6 to $6\frac{1}{2}$ cm in length when fully fed. In the early instars it is a dull green, marked with longitudinal lines of greenish-white, and during this stage it can be found feeding on the upper sides of the leaves, even in daylight. Later it changes to a dull greyish-brown and tends to conceal itself during the day and feed at night. Along the sides runs a broad creamy-buff band decorated with dark brown bars, running obliquely upwards, but sloping towards the head and not towards the tail-end of the body as in the Privet Hawk and others. The head is small and the horn short and after the skin turns dark the horn disappears and is replaced by a round yellow disc with a black, shiny knob, rather like a button, in the centre. After it has finished feeding the caterpillar often wanders restlessly for quite a long time before it pupates among rubbish on the ground.

The Pupa. The pupa is rather small and slender with two prominent tubercles at the front of the body and a well-developed tongue case. The spike at the tail is long and thin with a double point. In captivity breeders have found that the pupae cannot stand moist conditions and must be kept very dry.

The Adult Moth. The moth varies a great deal in size, from a wing-span of only $3\frac{1}{2}$ to 6 cm. The ground colour of the fore-wings is a clear medium green. The outer margin of the wing is indented and irregular. A dark green band, with lighter shading at the edges, runs across the fore-wing and encloses a distinct black discoidal spot. Between this band and the body the wing is rather grey-green. The hind-wing, which also has a rather wavy edge, is yellow with a brown margin. The head and the sides of the thorax are olive-green and the rest of the body grey-brown. The grey antennae are club-shaped and end in a hook. Under a magnifying glass it can be seen that the eyes have strong lashes. Several varieties occur, including a grey form and a pale brown type with a reddish-yellow band across the wings,

Hemaris croatica

Haunts. This moth occurs only in the south-eastern parts of Europe, in Yugoslavia, Bulgaria and Greece, and also in Asia Minor and the Caucasus.

The Egg. The eggs are laid singly on wild scabious or on species of *Asperula* and *Cephalaria*.

The Caterpillar. The larvae can be found in June and July and again as a second brood in early autumn. They vary a great deal in colour and many different forms are known. The ground colour may be a dirty yellowish-white or almost any shade of green or a lighter or darker shade of brick red. A white stripe runs along either side. The horn is usually more or less orange in colour and there are dark patches between the sucker feet.

The Pupa. The rather small pupa is reddish-brown and lies on the ground among rubbish in a slight web.

The Adult Moth. This is a close relation of the Bee Hawks, although, because its wings are not transparent, it has in the past been wrongly classified as more closely akin to the Hummingbird Hawk-moth. It is about the same size as the Broad-bordered Bee Hawk. The thorax and the greater part of the fore-wings are a bright olive-green with a band of reddish-brown along the outer margin. The hind-wings are entirely red-brown. The abdomen is decorated with a wide band of this same red-brown colouring and the fan-shaped tail tufts are black. This is a day-flying moth which is fond of visiting flowers.

Breeding Hawk-Moths in Captivity

The hawk-moths are, generally speaking, fairly easy to breed in captivity, although in a country like Britain the migrant species are often infertile and if larvae are obtained they frequently die from lack of sun and warmth. In a more suitable climate, however, such as in southern Europe, they too can usually be reared without much difficulty, from the egg to the perfect insect, provided they are supplied with suitable growing food. The mating of moths in captivity is perhaps the greatest problem and it is here that most would-be breeders fail. Comparatively little is known about the mating habits of some of the larger hawk-moths such as the Death's-head, the Convolvulus, the Oleander Hawk and the Silver-striped Hawk, and they may well need special conditions which are not easily simulated in captivity.

My own experience has been, in the main, with the native British hawk-moths, although I have on occasions also reared one or two of the migrants, but never right through the complete life cycle from one generation to the next. With native insects the problems of providing additional warmth and artificial sunlight do not arise, and successful breeding depends more on constant day-to-day attention and adequate feeding than on any specialized treatment.

For a great many years I have bred Poplar and Lime Hawks, Eyed Hawks, Privet Hawks, Pine Hawks and Elephant Hawks, season after season, overwintering the pupae and starting up again in the spring. I have found that the most satisfactory way of storing the pupae over winter is to keep them in closed tins in a cool larder. In this way they do not lose moisture, which is one of the main reasons why many pupae, kept indoors, dry up and die, and they are protected against such enemies as clothes moth larvae and mice, which frequently attack hibernating pupae left in breeding cages.

In the spring, usually about the middle of April, the overwintering pupae are taken out of their tins and laid on moss, over a few inches of moist peat, in breeding cages in an unheated greenhouse. These cages measure about two feet square and three feet in height and are covered in muslin, with a mosquito netting top so that air can pass freely through them. A few bare twigs are placed among the pupae, leaning up against the sides of the cages, so that the moths can quickly find some support to climb up when they emerge. The netting or muslin also provides a good foothold. No breeding cage should have slippery sides because if a newly emerged moth has difficulty in climbing upwards and loses its foothold and falls, the chances are that its wings will be crippled and malformed. In warm, dry weather the pupae are given a daily damping with a fine spray, to prevent them drying up, but no wetting is done if the weather is cold or damp, as pupae can also easily be killed by too much water.

When the moths begin to emerge they are left undisturbed until the early evening. Before they begin to fly they are distributed in a number of cages, not more than three males and the same number of females in

Lime Hawk-moths emerging in
a breeding cage. The pupae lie on
moist peat and the moths crawl up
the sticks to dry their wings.

each cage. If there are more males than females, two males are often put in a cage with a single female. Generally the males tend to emerge first, and the females a few days later. The ventilators of the greenhouse are left open so that a current of air may pass through the house and at dusk the males begin to fly, the females sitting quietly, with their scent organs protruding, 'calling' and waiting for the males. With this treatment Poplar, Lime and Eyed Hawks normally pair quite naturally, although unusually low night temperatures may sometimes make the moths sluggish and reluctant to mate.

The paired moths remain together throughout most of the following day, the males hanging, head downwards, the females clinging to the side or top of the cage. They should on no account be disturbed by touching or handling the cage, and if for some reason the cage must be opened, this should be done very carefully, so as not to cause too much noise or vibration. In the mid-afternoon Lime Hawks will separate and at dusk the other two species, the Poplars and the Eyed Hawks part, the male dropping down and flying off, while the female, after a short interval, also begins to fly and starts to lay her eggs. None of these three hawk-moths need to be fed on nectar or sugar syrup. The eggs are fully developed in their bodies when they emerge and are laid in four or five days as a rule. The males will often pair a second time and can be put in cages with fresh females the same evening.

If a female of any of these hawk-moths is left in the breeding cage, she will lay her eggs on the muslin and on the side of the cage, but in practice I have found it most convenient to confine each female, as soon as she has parted from the male, in a cardboard box. This means that the breeding cage must be visited at dusk to capture the fertile females. Shoe boxes, with their slightly rough interior, are ideal—the lids are heavy enough to prevent the moths from escaping and yet they are not airtight. Sometimes I place a piece of muslin across the box and put the lid on over this, to provide the moth with a good foothold, and the eggs are then usually laid on the muslin, rather than on the box itself. It is not necessary to put any leaves of the food plant in the box, although occasionally I have found this is a help, if a female seems slow in laying. In cold weather it is also a good idea to move the boxes into a warm room.

On the Butterfly Farm we always label each box with the date on which the female begins to lay. The time of hatching varies with the weather, and in a normal spring, if the boxes are kept in a fairly cool place, the incubation period is usually just three weeks, but it can be speeded up by raising the temperature. The colour of the eggs always

L. Hugh Newman inspecting a 'sleeve' on the
limb of a poplar in the grounds of his breeding
establishment at Westerham in Kent.

changes to some extent just before hatching, when the embryo larvae
can be seen through the shells, so a daily inspection will give some idea
when hatching is imminent.

I have found that all these moths do much better if they are reared
on growing food, rather than on twigs of their food plants standing in
water. Young leaves, early in the summer, when the eggs hatch, are
too sappy and delicate to remain fresh in water for more than a day,
and by far the best method of rearing these caterpillars is to 'sleeve'
them out of doors; this can be done very easily if you have the appropriate trees or bushes growing in your garden. Failing this, cut food will
have to be used, but it is not as good and entails far more work and
trouble.

114

The so-called 'sleeve' is merely a piece of thin muslin or cheese cloth sewn into a tube shape. The length and width must be governed by the size of the limb that is to be covered and of course by the number of caterpillars one wishes to rear. Overcrowding must always be avoided. The sleeve is slipped over a branch with plenty of clean healthy leaves and is tied firmly round it at the lower end, with a piece of strong twine. A day or two before the eggs are due to hatch the whole shoe box is placed inside this sleeve, after removing the lid, or if the eggs have been laid on a piece of muslin, we drape this among the twigs. The shoe box should, if possible, be put in upside down, so that it does not fill with water if it rains. The sleeve is then tied firmly at the top end to prevent the entry of earwigs, spiders and birds, and the caterpillars are left to hatch and crawl down on the leaves of their own accord.

Once the boxes have been put outside on the growing food we normally leave them untouched for about a week and then the sleeves are opened for inspection. If all the eggs have hatched the box is removed, but sometimes, if the moth has laid its eggs over a fairly long period, they do not all hatch at the same time, and then it must be put back into the sleeve until hatching is completed. The young caterpillars will by then have crawled out among the leaves and begun to feed. By turning the leaves over they can be found, nearly always clinging to the mid-rib on the underside of the leaf.

Regular inspection of the sleeves will show when the time has arrived to change over to another branch. The caterpillars should never be allowed to strip the branch completely bare, or to remain in a sleeve where the leaves have become dirty and sticky through the activities of aphids, or perhaps have shrivelled or turned yellow during a spell of hot dry weather. As soon as the foliage has become sparse or in any way discoloured or unhealthy-looking, the caterpillars must be moved.

The system which we generally adopt on the Butterfly Farm is to cut off the entire branch, thus pruning the tree at the same time as changing the sleeve. The whole bag is then laid on a big table and opened at one end. The twigs are pulled out, one by one, and the caterpillars are picked off, if possible without any direct handling, by cutting or breaking off the leaves on which they rest. These are dropped into a clean muslin bag which has already been tied up at one end, and when they have all been collected and transferred, the new sleeve is slipped over another suitable branch and firmly tied into place. This process often has to be repeated a number of times, depending on how many larvae one is rearing and on the size of the sleeve. As the caterpillars grow larger and firmer they can withstand handling better, but one must always be

A 'sleeve' on a poplar tree has been opened to show a fully fed Poplar Hawk caterpillar hanging on a twig.

careful not to injure them or tear their sucker feet and claspers when pulling them off the twigs. At all times the sleeve must be kept free of dirt and when the larvae are getting big it is necessary to open the sleeve every day and tip out the frass, which collects at the bottom. This is specially important in wet weather.

Lime Hawks will feed happily on any kind of cultivated lime tree and also, as an alternative, on elm. Poplar Hawks will eat any kind of poplar and also aspen, and the Eyed Hawk-moth caterpillars will also feed on poplar, willow, sallow or apple, preferably on cooking varieties such as Bramley seedling.

When the caterpillars are full-fed arrangements must be made for pupation. It is very easy to tell when Lime Hawk larvae are ready to pupate, because the colour change is very pronounced, but Poplar Hawks and Eyed Hawks are more difficult. They do not turn pink or brown but simply become rather more dull in colour, with a slight brownish tinge,

An assembling cage is placed on the roof of a shed near the poplar trees. A virgin female Poplar Hawk is put into the cage and her scent will attract wild males. In this way fresh breeding stock is obtained.

and the best indication is their diminishing size and their behaviour. They leave the food and try to push their way out of the sleeve, collecting either at the bottom or in the folds at the top, and when they are handled they twist and jerk from side to side and feel very firm and springy to the touch.

During the restless period just before pupation, the larvae sometimes eat their way out of the sleeves, and unless they are put into very strong containers with well-fitting lids, they will try to escape. We have found that the most satisfactory way of dealing with Lime Hawks is to put the fully fed caterpillars in a large wooden box or tub, filled with pieces of soft, crumpled cotton material, such as old clean muslin sleeves. The larvae crawl in among the folds, draw the material around themselves with a few strands of silk and then pupate, each one in its own compartment, so to speak, and without disturbing each other.

The Poplar Hawks and the Eyed Hawks prefer to burrow, and the best and safest material to give them is granulated peat, which is practically sterile, soft and so light that there is no danger of malformed pupae. Strong wooden boxes, such as old ammunition boxes, with heavy lids, are ideal, but failing this, or for only a small number of larvae, flower pots are excellent too, but a plate or a tile or piece of slate should be put across the top to prevent the caterpillars from escaping, as they sometimes change their minds even after they have burrowed down and come up again and wander off somewhere else.

It is a great mistake to crowd too many larvae into one container. For some reason the majority of them like to pupate in a corner, and if the box is overcrowded, so many larvae will pack down close together that they disturb each other, and the result will be malformed and mis-shapen pupae. The ideal is one caterpillar in each flower pot, but if a box is used the number will depend on its size. We usually limit the number in a standard ammunition box to fifty. After the last caterpillar has 'gone down' the date is marked on the box, the lid is firmly closed and it is left untouched for at least a fortnight or sometimes three weeks. By the end of this time all the larvae will have pupated and become firm and they can then be unearthed and sorted. I never keep any malformed or abnormal pupae for breeding, and all those which are to be stored away for the winter are put, first of all, in shoe boxes for a couple of weeks. This gives them time to become really hard and any excess moisture can evaporate.

If there has been any disease among the larvae, newly turned pupae will often go soft and rotten, and as this generally happens fairly soon, the pupae can again be carefully sorted and then all those which appear to be perfectly healthy and are of a good size are stored away in tins, while the doubtful ones are discarded. It is wise to open the tins and inspect the pupae at intervals in case any more of them have died later. An unpleasant smell when the tin is opened is a warning of danger and any pupae which look unnaturally dark or feel soft to the touch should be removed. A healthy pupa is firm and always very cool. A soft or brittle pupa which feels warm to the touch is nearly always dead.

The main difference between breeding the three native Hawk-moths mentioned above and the other British Hawk-moths is in the treatment of the adults. The Privet Hawk, the Pine Hawk and the two Elephant Hawks all need feeding if they are to do well. Their eggs are not fully developed when they hatch and unless the females are provided with plenty of nectar-bearing flowers, they will lay very few eggs, or if they do lay reasonably well, many of them will be infertile.

The Privet Hawks are left to emerge and pair in the breeding cages, in the same way as the Poplar and Lime Hawks, but as soon as they have parted in the late afternoon, the females are put into round wooden tubs lined with muslin and with a cover of mosquito netting. A bunch of flowers, usually red valerian, is put into each tub, and also some sprigs of green privet. Sustained by feeding and encouraged by the presence of the privet leaves, they generally lay very well, on both the netting and the muslin as well as on the leaves. Several females can be put in each tub and the flowers must be changed every other day. In this way it is possible to obtain a large number of eggs. These normally hatch within ten days to a fortnight, as the weather by then is warming up. We sleeve the larvae out of doors, either on privet, lilac or ash, and they seem to feed equally well on all three of these food plants. The Pine Hawks are treated in exactly the same way, being given flowers, preferably honey-suckle, as well as twigs of Scots pine. We always prefer to use round tubs rather than square breeding cages for the females to lay in, because they do not batter themselves so much while flying, or get wedged into corners, as often happens in an ordinary cage.

For the Elephant Hawks I have evolved a different technique, which entails the preparation, early in the season, of a large outdoor flight cage, covered with fine netting and planted with rosebay willowherb or bed-straw. By the time the moths emerge, the plants are in full growth, and as soon as the moths have dried their wings they are taken out of the emerging cages in the greenhouse and liberated into these big outdoor cages. Cut flowers are provided in jars of water and renewed every two or three days, and the moths are then left entirely alone.

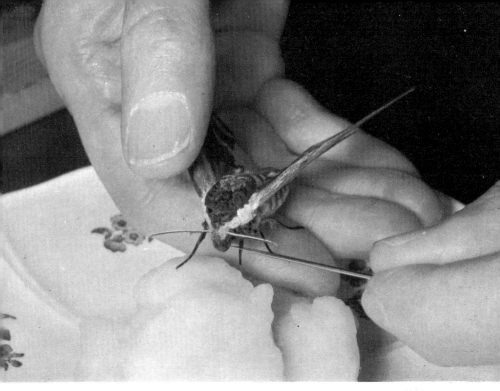

A moth that is becoming weak can often be revived by forcible feeding. The tongue is gently unrolled with a needle and placed on a pad of cotton wool soaked in honey and water.

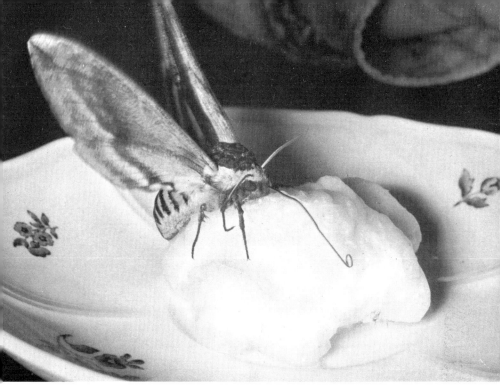

Once the moth tastes the sweet liquid it will stay and feed without being held. Energy is quickly regained and here a female Privet Hawk prepares to fly after her meal.

One never sees them paired because they only remain mated for a short period during the night, but this system invariably results in a large number of fertile eggs being laid on the plants and here the caterpillars are left to feed up on the growing plants. Very often, especially with the large Elephant Hawk-moths which eat a great deal, the cage is stripped before the larvae are full-fed, and then we have to resort to cut food. I have found that the caterpillars can be reared like this, although not without losses, if they are kept in cool shaded cages and given fresh food every other day without fail, whether the old food has been eaten or not. Stale, waterlogged food is fatal and always leads to disease.

The Elephant Hawks do not wander far when they want to pupate, nor do they burrow into the ground, and the best method is to cover the floor of the cage, specially round the edges, with a good layer of moss. The larvae will push their way into this, make their flimsy silken cocoons and change into pupae.

I have never attempted to rear the two Bee Hawks in captivity right from the pupal stage, but, judging from their habits in the wild, they would need both sunlight and flowers as well as growing scabious or honeysuckle and probably a large cage would be necessary in order to get pairings. The larvae are quite simple to rear on growing food, by using scabious plants in pots or sleeving strands of honeysuckle.

The migrant hawks are a much more difficult problem, and most entomologist agree that the larvae need plenty of sun and warmth. Spurge Hawks will feed and grow rapidly on various kinds of spurge, being especially fond of sea spurge and cypress spurge, but in my experience the plants must be growing in soil, and not standing in water. When fed on cut food, they seem unable to pupate and many die even before they reach their full size. Often, in cases where cut food has to be used, it is better simply to throw a supply of leaves into the cage at intervals during the day and renew it when it wilts, rather than put sprigs in water, but this system is very wasteful and not always possible if there is only a limited supply of food available.

A successful attempt at rearing the Hummingbird Hawk-moth was reported in the *Amateur Entomologist* some years ago. The correspondent who described it had captured a female moth hovering over flowers and put it in a breeding cage. He then provided it with some flowers and a bunch of bedstraw in a pot of water, and the moth began to lay. He noticed particularly that until the bedstraw shoots were raised up, so that they nearly touched the top of the cage, the moth laid on the muslin and on the wooden sides and did not fly down on to its proper food plant.

This idiosyncrasy is very marked with many moths and I have found, again and again, that unless the food plant is raised well up in the cage it will be ignored, because the moths nearly always flutter about as near the top as possible in their efforts to escape.

Overcrowding is a great danger to larvae in captivity. None of the hawk-moths are naturally gregarious and to keep a large number together in a cage or a sleeve, invariably causes trouble. Quite often, under such crowded conditions, the larvae will eat each other's tail horns, and it is quite common to see two almost full-grown hawk-moth larvae biting and apparently fighting each other. This is a sure indication that they prefer to be alone or at least well spaced out on the food plant. Hygiene is important also, and both cages and sleeves must be kept clean. Daily attention is necessary after the first week or two, even when the caterpillars are in quite a big sleeve. If the frass is allowed to accumulate and rainy weather sets in, the whole sleeve becomes foul and dirty water drips on the leaves, contaminating everything. Long spells of wet and chilly weather are very bad for all the hawk-moth larvae, even our own natives, but especially so for the migrant species, which require a dry warm atmosphere to thrive. A few showers of rain do no harm, but a cold spell will often encourage any latent disease to break out.

Hawk-moth caterpillars are subject to various diseases, both bacterial and of the virus type. The most common disease is that known popularly as 'wilt disease' when apparently healthy larvae suddenly collapse and become mere empty skins, their body contents dissolving into fluid. Another disease shows itself as a gradual shrinking in size. In this case the larvae may survive for quite a long time before dying.

It is sometimes possible to recognize an unhealthy caterpillar at a fairly early stage, by its appearance. The colours become dull and the larva takes on a dirty look, often being streaked with brown, especially round the feet. There may be signs of diarrhoea, the caterpillar may feel flabby to the touch and it does not feed with its normal healthy appetite. Difficulty in skin casting is another bad sign and it is wise to remove any caterpillars which look 'off-colour' and put the remaining ones into a fresh clean sleeve. It is quite common for epidemics to break out among hawk-moth larvae and when this happens very few will survive or make the change to pupae successfully. If they do succeed they often die afterwards and any moths which are reared from an infected brood should not be used for breeding, as they will almost certainly pass on the disease to their progeny. Good healthy stock is of the greatest importance and if there is disease in the strain no amount of care and trouble will be of much avail, while thoroughly healthy larvae will often survive a certain amount of neglect.

If one rears or captures a female hawk-moth it is often possible to find her a mate by assembling, and it is certainly worth trying this method with all the more common species. The female should be put either by an open window, or preferably right out of doors in a cage with sides of netting. On a suitable evening—warm, with a slight breeze blowing—males are almost certain to come to the cage if there are any in the neighbourhood, and when they arrive the door can be opened so that they can gain admission. It is very unlikely that the female will take to the wing and escape if she has not yet paired and is not disturbed after her dusk flight. Alternatively the males can be caught in a net and put into the cage. Another method is to tether the female to the outside of the cage with a piece of soft embroidery silk or cotton round her waist, threaded through the netting and tied on the inside. Secured in this manner she will be unable to escape, but any males which catch her scent can find her easily. The danger to guard against when this method is used is of birds finding the two moths in the early morning, and the cage should, if possible, be removed to a safe place under cover as soon as a pairing is noticed.

It is unwise to try to force hawk-moth pupae out of season if the moths are to be used for breeding. Forcing often results in the moths being abnormal and they are particularly liable to be sterile because the reproductive organs have not had time to develop properly. It is possible, however, to get many of our native hawk-moths, and most of the migrant species, to emerge in mid-winter if desired. The indigenous pupae must be given a period of about two months of pre-cooling before forcing begins. I have found that storing the pupae in an ordinary domestic refrigerator from October to the middle of December has a good effect and they are then transferred, first to gentle warmth and then into a forcing cupboard kept at about 76°–80°F. when they will usually begin to emerge within three or four weeks. The percentage of cripples and abnormal insects is higher than if they are allowed to emerge at their natural season. It is important to moisten the pupae regularly with tepid water, otherwise the dry warmth will kill them during the period of forming up. With pupae of the migrant species pre-cooling is often unecessary and may, indeed, be harmful, because in their native countries they are very seldom subjected to low temperatures. As already mentioned in the individual chapters, many of these moths emerge naturally within a few weeks of pupating and the only forcing that is necessary in Britain is to keep them in a warm place indoors, such as above a stove or boiler or in an airing cupboard. Nevertheless their emergence is sometimes very erratic, and on occasions no amount of forcing appears to have any effect.

Many entomologists are interested in hybridizing hawk-moths and a good deal of experimental work has been done particularly in Switzerland, France and Germany. A number of hybrids have been reared, both between species and between local races, and also some secondary hybrids. Unlike hybrid plants, which usually exhibit what is known as hybrid vigour and are stronger and larger than their parents, hybrid hawk-moths are nearly always delicate and difficult to rear, and although the larvae may feed up quickly and appear healthy, very many of them fail to turn into pupae, or die in the pupal stage before emerging.

Breeders have also noticed that the larvae show what is known as 'anticipation' in reaching certain stages in their development earlier than the larvae of either of the parent species. The resulting moths are not always sterile, but their fertility is reduced, especially in the females, and this degeneration of the reproductive organs becomes very marked if attempts are made to continue breeding from successive generations. The same thing happens even when it is only a case of crossing distinct geographical races of the same species.

Some hybrids occur in nature and have been found wild on occasions, but they are always rare. The greatest number discovered are of the hybrid between *Celerio vespertilio* and *Celerio Euphorbiae*, known as *Hybrid epilobii*. They have been found both in southern France and in Germany in areas where these two moths occur together. Others are *Hybrid kindervateri*, a cross between the Spurge Hawk and the Bedstraw Hawk; *Hybrid pernoldi*, the result of a cross between a male Elephant Hawk and a female Spurge Hawk; and *Hybrid standfussi*, the hybrid between the Small and the Large Elephant Hawk. A great many more have been produced in captivity and the results of breeding experiments, compared to suspected hybrids caught in the wild, have confirmed that cross breeding does occur now and then.

On the whole the hybrids appear to be a mixture between their parents, both in size and markings, but cases are known where the characteristics have not fused, but appear side by side, in a sort of mosaic pattern. Quite often also, the fore-wings and thorax resemble the female parent, while the hind-wings and abdomen are like the male. The larvae also show a mixture of parental characteristics and sometimes feed on the maternal, sometimes on the paternal food. There seems to be no general rule in this respect.

Breeding Hawk-Moths in Captivity

To obtain hybrids in captivity it is essential to have males and females of the two different species emerging at the same time. If they do not do this naturally, it is sometimes possible to retard the earlier species a little, by keeping the pupae cool, and this is generally better than resorting to forcing. The cross-pairing which is most often attempted in Britain is a mating between a male Eyed Hawk-moth and a female Poplar Hawk, and this is comparatively easy to secure.

In order to stimulate the males, it is necessary to have females of their own species present, either in a cage close by, or even in the same cage. I have secured this pairing on several occasions by placing two Eyed Hawk males and a female of both the Poplar and the Eyed Hawk together in one cage. The males, stimulated by the scent of the female Eyed Hawk, attempt to pair, one mating with its own species and the other with the female Poplar Hawk. These pairings are, however, only occasionally fertile, and if the larvae do hatch, they are by no means easy to rear. The resulting moths are known scientifically as *Smerinthus hybridus*.

The fore-wings resemble those of the Poplar Hawk fairly closely, while on the hind-wings appears an eye-spot, which, however, is neither as large nor as colourful as that of the Eyed Hawk, and the ground colour of the area in which the spot is situated is rust-red as in the Poplar Hawk, not rosy-pink as in the Eyed Hawk. The hybrid tends to be slightly smaller than either of the parents.

An entomologist named House, who first described this hybrid in the *Transactions* of the Entomological Society of London in 1842, remarked: 'I have often indulged in fanciful ideas respecting this production but I never conceived such an unfinished painting as it is; this is not nature improved by art, but nature sadly defaced by art, as the beauty of both species is, in great measure, lost.' He also noticed what many others have since confirmed, that a great many of the hybrids appear to be gynandromorphs and the females, especially, often have deformed genitalia, showing male characteristics. As far as I know, no secondary hybrids have ever been reared, which indicates that they are always sterile. The adult moths nearly always emerge soon after pupating, in about a month's time, instead of overwintering in the pupal stage.

It is also possible to obtain, without difficulty, the opposite cross-pairing, betwen a male Poplar Hawk and a female Eyed Hawk, but in this case the eggs rarely hatch, although the embryo larvae may develop inside the shells. For some reason they seem unable to break out, possibly because the Eyed Hawk egg is considerably smaller than that of the Poplar Hawk and the larvae may outgrow the space before they are ready to hatch and die within the shell. A small number have been reared, however, after most carefully cutting open the eggs with a razor blade and releasing them. The resulting hybrid, named *Lathoe hybrid rothschildii*, is very similar to the other hybrid between these two species. The hybrid between a male Lime Hawk and a female Eyed Hawk has also been obtained at least once in captivity, but this is much more difficult.

In the 1940s a Swiss entomologist, Herr Meyer, conducted a series of experiments in producing artificial hybrids. This was done, not by cross-pairing, but by carefully drawing off some of the body fluid from a pupa of one species and injecting it with a hypodermic syringe into another of a different species. By this highly artificial laboratory method he obtained many very remarkable and interesting moths of mixed blood.

Making a Collection of Hawk-Moths

The insects in a collection should be in good condition, and with the hawk-moths it is usually possible to obtain pupae. of at least the more common species and then breed them out to produce perfect specimens. Digging at the roots of trees during the winter, in places where the moths are known to occur, will often unearth a number of pupae. In the spring, at the time when the moths are emerging, it is sometimes well worth while to search the tree trunks during the day for fresh specimens which have crawled up to dry their wings. Limes and elm trees, poplars, apple trees, sallows and willows, and pine trunks in districts where the Pine Hawk is known to breed, are favourite sites for newly emerged moths. If a fresh female is found, it is usually possible to catch quite a number of males by the assembling method already mentioned in the previous chapter. A mixture of sugar, beer and treacle smeared on to posts or tree trunks may lure the Elephant Hawks to come and feed, and beds of scented, nectar-rich flowers in a garden are often an excellent hunting ground, especially in the late summer when the migrant hawk-moths are most likely to be on the wing.

The most popular method of collecting moths is by using a mercury vapour moth trap. Entomologists have been using this type of trap now for some fifteen years. It was invented by two brothers, H. S. and P. J. M. Robinson, and has proved so efficient that it has superseded all other older types of light trap. An electric bulb, filled with mercury vapour, is an intensely bright source of artificial light and its spectrum stretches much further towards the ultra-violet wave length than that of any other type of bulb. It is impossible to look directly at it without the protection of dark glasses, and even with them it causes discomfort. Although moths are apparently quite insensitive to red light, they react strongly to ultra-violet, which accounts for the extraordinary effect of this type of light on them. The old-fashioned traps usually sent out a beam of light in one direction only, but this modern one is so constructed that the light shines unhindered all round; and it is estimated that with a 125-watt bulb it will act in a circle with a radius of about seventy-five yards.

The trap itself is of a simple design. It consists of a shallow metal cylinder about two feet across and six inches high. A groove runs round the top and into this fits a truncated cone of transparent plastic material. The mouth of the cone holds a metal funnel, a foot in diameter, which tapers down to an opening some four inches wide. The bulb is held by a fixture just above this aperture, which is the only entrance to the trap. A flex, passing through a choke, to the nearest electric point, provides the power (the light can also be run off the generator of a car). As the moths come flying up to the light they fall down the funnel into the trap, which, to prevent overcrowding and damage to the moths, is lined with sheets of indented papiermâché, normally used for packing eggs. Being rough, this material gives insects a good foothold and the large area enables an enormous number of moths to settle in the trap without jostling each other.

Unless a captured hawk-moth is in good condition, or happens to be a very rare migrant or an aberration, it is a pity to include it in a collection, but all worn and damaged moths should be examined carefully to ascertain their sex, and it is always a good plan to keep females for some days in a breeding cage and supply them with flowers and the appropriate food plant for egg-laying. In the case of a rare moth, a chance of obtaining eggs should never be missed, and even if the female does damage herself while in captivity, she can still be set for the collection later and labelled, perhaps, as the parent of a series of perfect specimens bred from her eggs.

The best way of killing the large hawk-moths when they are wanted for a collection is to inject them with a drop or two of a saturated solution of oxalic acid through a hypodermic syringe. All chemists stock syringes of this kind. The moth is held firmly in the left hand with the wings closed above the back and the needle is inserted between the legs. Death is almost instantaneous. Alternatively a killing bottle can be used, but for big moths it will have to have a wide mouth. Experienced collectors usually prefer a bottle charged with cyanide of potassium, but this is a dangerous substance and a non-poisonous bottle may be preferred. A good bottle can be made simply by putting a layer of plaster of Paris at the bottom of a large jam jar, and fitting it with a lid or stopper which is air tight. Any killing agent such as carbon tetrachloride, ethyl acetate, ether or chloroform can be used. A few drops are poured on to the plaster, the moth is put into the bottle and this is then tightly closed. The moth

*L. Hugh Newman and Michael Dickens inspect
the mercury vapour moth trap in the morning
in the author's garden at Westerham, Kent.
It has been switched on during the night and
many moths have collected inside. Those wanted
for breeding are put into glass bottom 'pill boxes',
while the rest are left in the trap and released in
the evening just before dusk.*

130

must be left in the bottle for at least an hour, to make certain that it will not revive.

Before a moth can be incorporated in a collection it has to be set, with its wings, antennae and legs in the correct position. Good setting makes all the difference to the appearance of a collection, but it takes some practice before a beginner can spread the wings evenly on either side of the insect. A selection of setting boards of different sizes, proper entomological pins, setting tapes and strips, a setting needle and a curved pair of forceps are the equipment needed.

The best kind of setting boards are those made of cork, glued on a wooden base, and they should be quite flat. Curved boards were popular at one time but this type of setting is now quite out of date. Entomological pins are sold in many sizes, both white and black. Black pins look better, but are slightly more expensive. A beginner will do best to buy a box of mixed sizes. Ordinary dressmaking pins can be used for fixing the setting strips, but moths should always be pinned on proper entomological pins, which do not rust.

Before a moth can be set it must be in a perfectly limp and soft condition. It is quite useless to try and set a stiff dry insect, as the wings will not move into place and merely break and tear. If a moth is set shortly after killing it will still be limp, but if rigor mortis has set in the insect should be left in a closed tin or jar until this stiffness passes. A long-dead moth will have become dry and brittle and must first be relaxed before it can be set. Whenever possible it is wise to set hawk-moths as soon as convenient after killing, as freshly dead specimens are always easier to handle than older, relaxed insects.

There are various ways of relaxing moths. One very good method is to put a layer of damp sand in the bottom of a cake or biscuit tin and place the moths in the tin on a piece of blotting paper. They should not actually touch the sand, and must be examined frequently to see that they do not go mouldy. Twenty-four to thirty-six hours in a sand tin should be enough to relax even very dry specimens. A jar of crushed laurel leaves or a tin filled with the special relaxing mixture obtainable from entomological dealers can also be used.

Another very quick way of relaxing moths is by an injection of hot water. A hypodermic syringe is filled with plain hot water and the needle is inserted between the legs as for killing. A small quantity of water is injected and the moth is then put aside for a few minutes. As soon as the water has softened the casing of the body, the needle can be pushed further in and some more water injected. Most of this will spurt out from various parts of the body, but this will not harm the moth and after a period of ten or fifteen minutes, or possibly a little longer with a large and very dry insect, it will be limp and ready to set.

The first step in setting a hawk-moth is to mount it on a pin of suitable size. To do this, pick up the moth with the forceps and then transfer it to the left hand, between thumb and forefinger, with the wings closed and the head pointing outwards. Squeeze it gently to make the wings open and then pick up a pin of the right size in the forceps and push it through the middle of the thorax, not absolutely at right angles, but sloping very slightly forwards. The point of the pin should emerge between the second and third pair of legs on the underside and be pushed through so that about two-thirds of it protrudes underneath the body.

The size of the setting board must match the size of the moth, and the groove down the middle should be just wide enough to take the body comfortably. Unless the insect is correctly pinned into the groove, however, the setting will never look right. It must not be pushed down too far, otherwise the wings will 'spring up' when it is taken off the board, but on the other hand it must not be so high that the wings become set in an arched position. The pin should be pushed in just far enough in the middle of the groove for the body to rest in such a position that the wings lie flat on the board without any strain.

Now the actual setting can begin. First of all take a piece of narrow tape or silk ribbon and pin it securely with a fairly large pin to the top of the board, close to the groove on the right side. Do the same thing on the left, carrying the tape down across the wings of the moth and pinning it to the board again about half an inch beyond the wings, so that they are kept strapped to the board. Take a setting needle, which is merely a large needle fixed into a handle, in the right hand and with the left hand stretch the tape on the right side across the wings and keep it close to the board with your fingers. With the setting needle, push the right fore-wing upwards, until its lower margin is almost at right angles to the body of the insect. This can be done in two ways, either by inserting the needle into the thickest part of the wing, close to the body, or by sliding it under the wing near the front edge and lifting the wing gently into position. Care should be taken not to tear holes in the wing with the needle. When the fore-wing is in position, the hind-wing should be brought up in the same way, keeping the tape fairly firm all the time and pulling it quite taut the moment both wings are in place. Now drop the setting needle and insert two pins through the tape, one directly above and the other just below the wings. This will keep them firmly in place. The tape on the left side is then loosened, the same process of arranging the wings is repeated, and the tape is pinned down again. The left side is more difficult to set if you are right-handed, but with a little practice it can be mastered.

If the body of the moth is not quite straight it should be eased into the correct position and held in place by a pin on either side, or by two pins pushed in so as to cross underneath the body. A small piece of cotton wool pushed under the body will prevent it from drooping. The antennae should also be set in position, pointing forward at the angle at which they are held when the moth is alive, and kept in place by small pins on either side. Now the two front legs are brought forward with the setting needle and secured into position. The outer portion of the wings must also be flattened on to the board and this is done by pinning strips of tracing linen or cellophane, or even wide nylon ribbon, over them, inserting the pins, not through the wings, but close to the margins. Finally pin a small label with date and place of capture close to the moth.

If you start from the top of the board and work downwards, several moths can be set on the same board. When setting is completed the board should be put in a safe place away from dust and the attacks of mice, wasps, silver fish and other creatures that might ruin the insects. A clean, dry cupboard is usually a good place, but best of all is a special so-called setting house, which will admit air to dry the moths. A meat safe with walls of perforated zinc and a couple of shelves inside will do very well. The floor should be sprinkled with paradichlorbenzene crystals to keep away pests. Leave the moths on the board for several weeks, until they are thoroughly dry. Then remove the strips of cellophane or ribbon, the tapes and all pins around the body and antennae, and lift the moth with the forceps carefully off the board and put it into the collection.

Hawk-moths will keep indefinitely in good condition if they are carefully stored. Well-made wooden store boxes are ideal for a small collection. These boxes are made to fit very tightly so that no dust can enter and both halves are of equal depth and lined with cork, covered with white paper, so that insects can be pinned on either side. The moths should be arranged in the boxes in straight rows, each one with a data label at the bottom of the pin. This is a small square of paper or thin card, giving the date and place of capture and, if desired, the name of the collector. At the bottom of each row, or series of moths, there should be another larger label with the scientific and popular name.

Large collections are usually stored in cabinets specially made for the purpose. A good cabinet must have glass tops to the drawers, preferably of the kind that lift off, rather than slide, and the drawers ought to be interchangeable. They should slide in and out easily on runners, as jerking or pushing is apt to shake the moths and break off their antennae. To make a good cabinet is a skilled job and it is wise for an amateur not to try to tackle it himself, but to store his collection in boxes until he can buy a cabinet from a reliable cabinet-maker or entomological dealer.

A collection which is not properly looked after will soon deteriorate. Mites and museum beetles and the grubs of clothes moths may gain access and destroy the specimens, or they may develop mould or grease. The most usual trouble is mites. These creatures are so tiny that they can even get into well-made boxes and cabinets, and if they are left undisturbed they will soon cause the moths to fall to pieces, by eating at their wings and bodies. Many store boxes are fitted with a small compartment or cell in one corner which should be kept filled with crystals of paradichlorbenzene. Failing this, crystals can be wrapped in a piece of gauze and pinned in the corners of the box. Camphor or naphthaline crystals can also be sprinkled loose in the drawers of cabinets, but this is not advisable in store boxes which are moved about at different angles. All these precautions will help to keep mites at bay.

Another most destructive pest is the museum beetle, which often attacks insect collections stored in faulty boxes or cabinets. The grubs of these beetles bore right into the bodies of the moths, eating them away and leaving only a hollow shell. Their presence can easily be detected by the small heaps of dust which appear beneath the moths. Naphthaline has no effect on these beetles but they can be quite easily killed in boxes or drawers that are fairly air tight, by fumigating with carbon disulphide or tetrachloroethane, but as these are poisonous substances they must be used with care. A few drops poured into a corner of the drawer or on a small dish stood inside and left to evaporate in the closed box or drawer will kill all the grubs. The treatment should be repeated fairly frequently, as eggs laid amongst the insects will hatch and produce more grubs.

If a collection is stored in a dry place there should not be any trouble with mould, but occasionally, in damp rooms, specimens do turn mouldy and it is wise to keep a look-out for this and treat the trouble at once. The first thing to do is to get the boxes or the cabinet and the insects thoroughly dry by standing them in a warm room, but not too near a fire. A really mouldy insect is past saving, but if only small spots of mould have as yet appeared, they can be removed by methylated spirit or benzene applied on a small paint brush. To prevent mould from appearing again a small swab of cotton wool should be twisted round the head of a pin and then dipped in pure carbolic acid and pinned in a corner of the box. The acid will cause a severe burn if it touches the skin, so the pin should only be handled with forceps. When a collection is properly stored under dry conditions there is usually little likelihood of mould.

A much more prevalent trouble is grease, which, particularly in Poplar Hawks, gradually seeps through the abdomen of the insect and spreads out over the wings, darkening them and obscuring the colour and pattern. The best way to deal with moths which have deteriorated in this way is to immerse them completely in a wide-mouthed jar filled with carbon tetrachloride and leave them there for an hour or two, gently moving the jar from time to time so that the liquid flows across the wings of the moth. When the moth is taken out it should be pinned to a piece of cork and stood in a current of air. The liquid will quickly evaporate and the moth will be thoroughly de-greased and can then be put back into the collection.

Examples of pupae and larvae are also interesting and valuable in a collection. Empty pupal shells can be kept, but naturally they are not as good as complete, unbroken pupae. It is not necessary to have more than two, a male and a female, and they are best killed by dropping them into spirit. They can be taken out again after a few days and pinned in the cabinet. Larvae can also be preserved in spirit or formaldehyde, but the best way is to keep only their inflated skins, which can then be pinned into the store box or cabinet beside the moths and will last indefinitely. The so-called 'blowing' of larvae is not easy and it requires a good deal of practice to do it well. The process consists of emptying the larval skin of its contents and then inflating it with air while it is quickly dried in a miniature oven, until the skin retains its shape.

The necessary apparatus for blowing larvae can be obtained from entomological dealers and consists of a small metal oven heated by a spirit lamp, glass blowpipes fitted with spring clips to keep the skins attached to the pipes, a rubber tube with a double bulb for inflating and a wooden roller for emptying the skins before blowing. A round pencil may be used instead.

The late H. E. Hammond, who was a great expert in the art of blowing larvae, gave the following instructions. The best way of killing a caterpillar is by dropping it into spirit (95 per cent.), or ordinary methylated spirit. This will kill it in a few moments. The dead caterpillar should then be laid on several thicknesses of blotting paper on a perfectly flat surface, placed on its back with its head towards you. With the forefinger on the roller exert gentle pressure on the body, beginning close to the anus and pushing the body contents towards the anal opening. When the gut begins to protrude, prick it with a needle to allow the liquid to escape without bursting the skin of the larva. Move the roller a little further towards the head and roll again, repeating the process until the skin has been emptied of all its contents. The whole operation should be done very gently so that the skin is not damaged. Heavy rolling will destroy the colours. If the whole digestive tract does not come away simply by rolling, it must be pulled out completely with a pair of forceps and snipped off with scissors. The contents of the head cannot be rolled out.

The empty skin is now slipped over the end of the glass nozzle, which should be very lightly smeared with vaseline, and secured in place with the aid of the spring clip. A gentle squeeze on the inflator bulb will fill the skin with air. Care should be taken not to blow the skin up too much, because this will make the caterpillar look unnaturally big and fat and distort the markings on the skin. The inflated skin is then inserted through the hole in the side of the oven and kept filled with air while it dries. The oven must not be too hot or the skin will become scorched and discoloured. A hawk-moth caterpillar should normally take about eight minutes to become perfectly dry and set. The head dries last and to make certain that this too is perfectly dry it should be tested by a light touch with the finger from the front. If there is still some movement, drying is not quite complete and should be continued a little longer.

When the skin is dry it can be mounted, either on a thin twig of suitable length and thickness or on a piece of silk-covered wire bent to the right shape so that it fits between the legs of the caterpillar. Seccotine is the best adhesive to use. The wire or the twig is then fixed on to a pin with a data label and the caterpillar skin is ready for the collection. Larvae can be blown at various times during their life history, but the period just before moulting should be avoided, because the skin is then too thin to stand up to rolling without damage and when blown it becomes unnaturally distended. The best time is a day or two after the caterpillar has begun to feed again following a skin casting. Uniformly green caterpillars sometimes lose their colour when blown, but this can be restored by painting them with a dye of the appropriate colour dissolved in spirit. Water colours are not satisfactory as they cause distortion of the skin.

Gradually building up a collection by catching moths, hunting for caterpillars, eggs and pupae or by breeding specimens in captivity is a hobby which never loses its appeal. Breeding is particularly interesting, because it gives an insight into the complete life history of a species, which cannot be gained in any other way. Careful notes about the behaviour and appearance of caterpillars in different stages, the length of time between the instars, details of pupation and emergence all add tremendously to the interest and value of a collection. Journeys abroad often give an opportunity to get moths which there is a very small chance of finding in Britain, and the search for them adds tremendously to the enjoyment of a foreign holiday. Practice improves the insect hunter's eye, and a person who knows what he is looking for will see a moth or a caterpillar where a hundred other people would pass by without noticing anything at all.

And even when a collection is complete the interest of breeding remains and the collector may turn to experiments such as hybridizing or the comparison of colour forms among caterpillars. An increasing number of people now also devote their spare time to breeding both moths and butterflies in order to release them when the adults emerge. At a time when wild life is seriously threatened in many parts of the world by the spread of urban civilization and all its attendant dangers of pollution and poisoning, this is something really worth while. In the natural state only a very small percentage of the progeny of a female moth ever survive, even when conditions are good, but when protected from natural enemies in captivity, the majority have a chance of reaching maturity, and when released will appreciably increase the local population. The progeny of a single female, released every year, might well make the difference between the continued existence or the disappearance of a species in a certain locality.

Mass collecting of dead specimens is now a completely out-dated hobby. A few good examples of each species are quite enough for a representative collection. Observing and understanding the habits of the living moths is much more interesting and of far greater value than merely studying the anatomical details of set specimens.

Index

Index

Bedstraw (*Galium*)
  Broad-bordered Bee Hawk, 39
  Elephant Hawk, 30, 119
  Hummingbird Hawk, 93, 100
  Silver-striped Hawk, 89
  Striped Hawk, 82
Bedstraw Hawk (*Celerio galii*), 71, 74, 77–81, 82, 125
Bee-hives, entered by Death's-head Hawks, 51–2
Belgium
  Spurge Hawk, 75
Berkshire
  Bedstraw Hawk, 79
Berlin
  Oleander Hawk, 69
Bexleyheath, Kent
  Death's-head Hawk, 52
Bindweed (*Convolvulus sepium*)
  Convolvulus Hawk, 59, 63
  Elephant Hawk, 30
Birch
  Poplar Hawk, 26
Birchington, Kent
  Convolvulus Hawk, 62
Birmingham
  Bedstraw Hawk, 79
  Elephant Hawk, 79
  Oleander Hawk, 68
Black nightshade (*Solanum nigrum*)
  Death's-head Hawk, 56
Blowing larvae, 135–6
Blue plumbago
  Silver-striped Hawk, 91
Bog-bean (*Menyanthes trifoliata*)
  Elephant Hawk, 30
Boisduval (entomologist), on the Convolvulus Hawk, 60
Bournemouth, Hants
  Pine Hawk, 9

Bradford, Yorks
  Hummingbird Hawk, 100
Bramley seedling
  Eyed Hawk, 19, 117
Braunton Burrows, Devon
  Spurge Hawk, 73
Bristol
  Hummingbird Hawk, 98
Brittany
  Spurge Hawk, 72
Broad-bordered Bee Hawk (*Hemaris fuciformis*), 39–41, 42, 43, 110; breeding of, in captivity, 122
Bude, Cornwall
  Striped Hawk, 85
Bugle (*Ajuga reptans*)
  Broad-bordered Bee Hawk, 40
Bulgaria
  Hemaris croatica, 110

Cabinets, for storing large collections, 133–4
Cages, breeding, 112
Cannes, France
  Hummingbird Hawk, 96
Canterbury, Kent
  Convolvulus Hawk, 62
Capri, Isle of
  Spurge Hawk, 75
Carlisle, Cumberland
  Bedstraw Hawk, 77
Caucasus, the
  Celerio vespertilio, 104
  Hemaris croatica, 110
  Oak Hawk, 102
Cedrus deodara
  Pine Hawk, 12
Cedrus libani
  Pine Hawk, 12
Celerio euphorbiae (Spurge Hawk), 125

Index

Entomologist's Record, The, on the Convolvulus Hawk, 62
Epilobium
  Proserpinus proserpina, 108
Epilobium rosemarininifolium
  Celerio vespertilio, 104
Evening primrose (*Oenothera*)
  Elephant Hawk, 30
Eyed Hawk (*Smerinthus ocellata*), 4, 18–19, 22–4, 126, 127; breeding of, in captivity, 111, 113, 117, 118

Fangfoss, York
  Death's-head Hawk, 57
Farn, A. B., 74
Farnborough, Hants
  Spurge Hawk, 74
Field bindweed (*Convolvulus arvensis*)
  Convolvulus Hawk, 59
Field scabious (*Scabiosa arvensis*)
  Narrow-bordered Bee Hawk, 42
Finland
  Bedstraw Hawk, 77
  Convolvulus Hawk, 59
  Elephant Hawk, 30
  Hummingbird Hawk, 93
  Oleander Hawk, 66
  Pine Hawk, 7
  Poplar Hawk, 25
  Privet Hawk, 4
  Small Elephant Hawk, 36
Folkestone, Kent
  Convolvulus Hawk, 59
  Death's-head Hawk, 45
  Spurge Hawk, 73, 74
France
  Celerio hippophaes, 106
  Celerio nicaea, 101
  Celerio vespertilio, 104

Hummingbird Hawk, 100
Oak Hawk, 102
Oleander Hawk, 67, 68, 69
Pine Hawk, 7, 9
Poplar Hawk, 25
Spurge Hawk, 74
Striped Hawk, 85, 86
Fuchsias
  Elephant Hawk, 30
  Silver-striped Hawk, 89
  Striped Hawk, 82

Galway
  Lime Hawk, 13
Genista tinctoria
  Small Elephant Hawk, 36
Geranium
  Hummingbird Hawk, 95
Germany
  Celerio hippophaes, 106
  Death's-head Hawk, 56
  Lime Hawk, 13
  Oleander Hawk, 68
  Pine Hawk, 7
  Proserpinus proserpina, 108
  Striped Hawk, 85, 86
Gibraltar
  Hummingbird Hawk, 99
Glasgow
  Oleander Hawk, 68
Goedart, Jan, *Metamorphosis et Historia Naturae Insectorum,* 32
Great hairy willowherb (*Epilobium hirsutum*)
  Elephant Hawk, 30
Greece
  Celerio nicaea, 101
  Hemaris croatica, 110
  Spurge Hawk, 74
Greenford, Middlesex
  Oleander Hawk, 68

142

Index

Index

Index